SYSTEM 44

NEXTGENERATION

read | talk | write

44Book™

Secondary

Printed in the U.S.A.

ISBN-13: 978-0-545-50122-4

11 12 13 14   6938   24 23 22 21 20 19 18 17

4510002678

Houghton Mifflin Harcourt™

W9-AYH-371

Table of Contents

MODULES

1

LIFE ISSUES
Informational Text

2

SOCIAL STUDIES
Informational Text

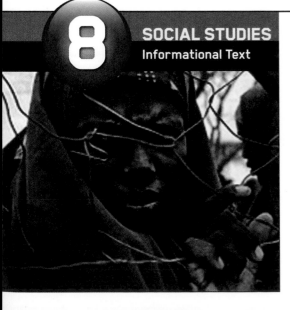

Welcome to the *44Book*

Get ready for the *44Book* by taking this quiz. After you finish each Module, check back to see if your ideas or opinions have changed.

START

1

SCHOOL MATTERS

Education usually leads to more knowledge and money. Which is more important? Why?

_____

_____

_____

_____

_____

SPECIAL FORCES

2

What makes a good soldier? Check the two most important qualities:

☐ brave   ☐ hard working

☐ cooperative   ☐ smart

☐ dedicated   ☐ strong

FAMOUS OR INFAMOUS?

4

Imagine you suddenly became famous. What might you like?

_____

_____

_____

_____

What might you dislike?

_____

_____

_____

_____

3

GAME ON!

Read each statement. Write **A** if you agree. Write **D** if you disagree.

_____ Science is important for making video games.

_____ Video games are a good way to learn.

_____ For video games, being fun is more important than teaching something.

FEAR FACTOR

5

What scares you the most? Rank these items (*1* = most scary; *3* = least scary).

_____ heights

_____ horror movies

_____ snakes

GUILTY UNTIL PROVEN INNOCENT

6

Write *A* if you agree. Write *D* if you disagree.

_____ Police should be able to stop anyone at any time.

_____ If you are arrested, that information should be public.

_____ Anyone who confesses to a crime should go to jail.

LOSING THEIR MINDS?

7

Read each statement. Write *T* if you think it is true. Write *F* if you think it is false.

_____ An athlete can play the next day after a head injury.

_____ Teenagers can die from concussions.

_____ Concussions can cause memory loss and personality changes.

Refugee Life: Starting Over

8

Think about the Module title "Refugee Life: Starting Over." Look at the photo above. What do you predict this Module will be about? Explain your reasoning.

_____

_____

_____

_____

_____

FINISH

Modules

SCHOOL MATTERS

How does education set you up for success?

School might be even more important than you think. For most people, more education means better jobs—and more money. Find out why school matters.

TEXT 1 Guidebook

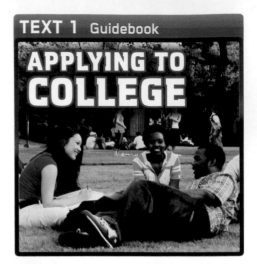

APPLYING TO COLLEGE

What do colleges want? Find out what can improve your chances.

TEXT 2 Brochure

Read Primary Sources

How can you find a college that is right for you? Reading brochures can help.

TEXT 3 Blog Post

Never Too Late

Meet a young woman who decided to go back to school.

Watch the video and complete the outline.

Anchor Word List

apply

community

evicted

future

graduation

I. Dawn Loggins was proud to go to her high school _graduation._

II. Dawn's family had been _____ from their home, and sometimes she had no place to live.

III. When it was time to _____ to college, she felt hopeful about getting in.

IV. Dawn's _____ of friends and teachers helped her get into college.

V. Now Dawn was sure that her _____ would be great.

○ **Discuss & Write**

Take turns asking and answering questions.

Q: What was one problem Dawn had growing up?

A: One problem Dawn had growing up was _____

_____

_____

_____

Q: What was one way that going to school helped Dawn?

A: One way that going to school helped Dawn was that _____

_____

_____

_____

Build Word Knowledge

Target Word
Read and rate each Target Word.*

Meaning
Complete the Target Word meanings.

Examples
Finish the Target Word examples below.

---

affect
af•fect
(verb)
p. 14

`1` `2` `3` `4`

to make a

_____

to somebody or

something

- Lack of sleep might **affect** my

_____

_____

- The way I _____

_____

can **affect** my grades.

---

employment
em•ploy•ment
(noun)
p. 23

`1` `2` `3` `4`

having a paying

_____

- _____

_____

is one way to find after-school

employment.

- I found **employment** _____

_____

---

success
suc•cess
(noun)
p. 14

`1` `2` `3` `4`

the achievement of

a _____

- My idea of **success** is _____

_____

_____

- To have **success** in sports, our

team needs to _____

_____

---

* Rating Scale

`1` = I don't know it at all.　　`3` = I think I know the word.
`2` = I've seen it or heard it.　　`4` = I know it and use it.

Word Families

Complete the meaning and examples for the Target Words.

Target Word	Meaning	Examples
succeed *suc•ceed* *(verb)* p. 25	to _____ a goal	• I hope to **succeed** (at/in) _____ _____ • To **succeed** in school, students need to _____ _____

Target Word	Meaning	Examples
successful *suc•cess•ful* *(adjective)* p. 14	having the planned _____	• I know I have been **successful** when _____ _____ _____ • A **successful** reader _____ _____

📖 Text-Based Questioning

Comprehension

How can activities like sports and band help you get into college?

These activities can help you get into

college because _____

_____

_____

_____

_____

🔍 Word Analysis

(Circle) the S.M.A.R.T. words that begin and end with one consonant sound. <u>Underline</u> words that begin or end with two consonant sounds blended together.

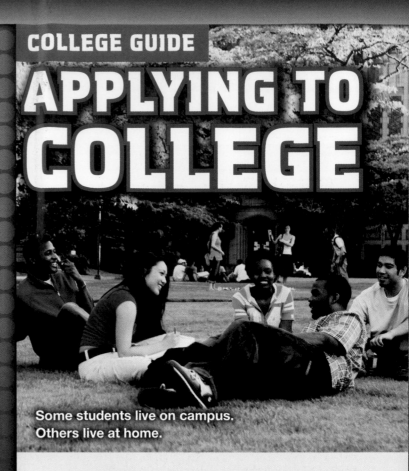

COLLEGE GUIDE

APPLYING TO COLLEGE

Some students live on campus.
Others live at home.

How can you **get** into college? You can work hard to achieve **success** in school. You can get involved in your community.

Academics
- Good grades **help**.
- **Most** colleges require you to take tests to get in. These include the SAT or ACT.

Activities
- Do you **play** a sport? Do you volunteer? Are you in a **club**?
- Activities show colleges that you will join their community.

Working hard to be **successful** in and out of school will **affect** your chances.

PREPARING YOUR APPLICATION

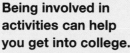 DO RESEARCH

Find schools that are a good fit for you. Visit school websites. Talk to your guidance counselor.

WRITE YOUR ESSAY

Show colleges what you have to offer. Explain what you've achieved.

MEET DEADLINES

Use a calendar to keep track.

Being involved in activities can help you get into college.

WORDS TO KNOW!

require: to make necessary

volunteer: to do work helping others for free

Word Count **120**   Lexile **290L**

Academic Discussion

Key Idea

Q: What is the key idea of the reading?

A: The key idea of the reading is _____.

> Several actions can help you get
>
> into _____

Important Details

Q: What items are important for getting into college?

A: _____ are important because _____.

> 1. Grades:
>
> 2. Tests:
>
> 3. Activities:

Summarize

Explain what colleges are looking for. Include the key idea and important details.

Stretch Text

Turn to page 188 to read nonfiction about how going to college can pay off.

Blending Sounds Into Words

Words are made up of individual sounds.

The single sounds are blended together to make a word.

These letters make the sounds /g/, /e/, /t/. Blended together, that's **get**.

Oh, I get it!

Blend It

Listen to the sound each letter stands for. Then blend the sounds together to make a word. Write the word on the line.

1. m a n
_____

2. g o t
_____

3. n o d
_____

4. th e n
_____

5. n e s t
_____

6. t u s k
_____

7. s t o ck
_____

8. s p i ll
_____

9. b l e n d
_____

Picture Perfect

**Listen to the sounds in each word. Blend the sounds together.
Then write the word beside its picture.**

1. sob

2. sun

3. jet

4. pin

5. neck

6. map

 _____

 _____

 _____

 _____

 _____

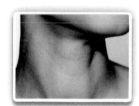 _____

Sentence Solver

Choose the correct words to complete the sentences.

1. We _____ use this _____ to cool the room. (fan, can)

2. It is too _____ to wear this _____ (hot, hat)

3. Please bring _____ my _____ (back, bag)

4. We _____ down the hill on a _____ (sled, slid)

Write an Informative Paragraph

Prompt | *What can help you get into college?*

Prewrite

Review Text 1 on pages 14–15. ★Star at least two actions that can help you get into college. Write down two examples from the text.

My Notes

Text Evidence	In My Own Words
"Good grades help."	Working hard in school is important.

Academic Discussion

Take turns asking and answering questions with a partner.

Q: What do colleges look for?

A: Colleges look for students who have _____.

Q: What else can students do to get into college?

A: Students can also _____ to get into college.

Read an example of nouns. Then use your notes and the writing frame to answer the prompt.

Nouns

A noun is a person, place, or thing.

Working hard can help you get into ___*college.*___
(noun)

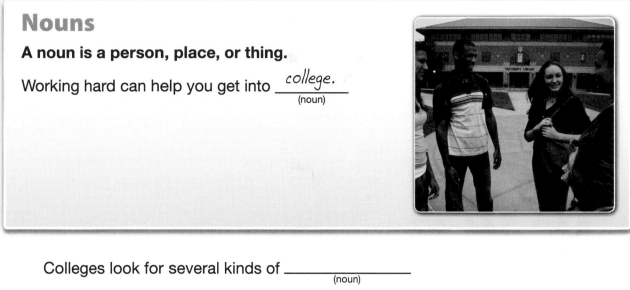

Colleges look for several kinds of _____
(noun)

Good _____ can help students get into college.
(noun)

Colleges also look for students who do well on _____
(noun)

Finally, having many _____ can improve students'
(noun)

applications. _____ consider many factors when they
(noun)

decide whom to admit.

Read your writing and check your spelling. Make sure your responses are nouns.

Read Primary Sources

How can you find the right college? A brochure can help. Colleges create them to **recruit** new students. Read this brochure that describes the University of Texas at San Antonio.

We Are UTSA And We Are You

You are ready for the next big step. You are searching for a place to grow, learn and live. You want to meet new people, discover great ideas and fulfill your dreams.

We are The University of Texas at San Antonio. We are excitement and challenges, inspiration and discovery—your first choice for world-class education, lifelong friendships and fun. We are global economies and the arts—your path to ideas, diversity and culture. We are a community of scholars, achievers and leaders. We are passion and we are change.

UTSA is your access to excellence. We are a top-tier university creating new knowledge through dialogue and discovery among our faculty and students. UTSA is serving society through our colleges, programs and initiatives by encouraging the best in all of us. We are enriching your collegiate experience through a vibrant student life, first-class facilities and Division I sports programs. We are degrees of success for people from Texas, the nation and the world.

We are The University of Texas at San Antonio. We are Roadrunners—and we are you.

Build Word Knowledge

Target Word Read and rate each Target Word.*	Meaning Complete the Target Word meanings.
recruit re•cruit (verb) [1] [2] [3] [4]	to get someone to join a _____, team, or other group
facility fa•cil•i•ty (noun) [1] [2] [3] [4]	a _____ that has a particular purpose

* Rating Scale [1] = I don't know it at all.   [3] = I think I know the word.
[2] = I've seen it or heard it.   [4] = I know it and use it.

Analyze

Use the brochure to answer the questions.

1. What images does the brochure include?

   The brochure includes images of _____

   _____

2. How might those images help the college recruit students?

   The images might help the college recruit students because _____

   _____

3. What other information from the text might encourage you to choose this college?

   One piece of information that might encourage me to choose this college is that

   _____

   _____

Text-Based Questioning

Comprehension

Why did Rashida Harris drop out of school?

Rashida dropped out of school because she

_____

_____

_____

_____

_____

Word Analysis

(Circle) the S.M.A.R.T. words with two sounds. Underline the words with three sounds.

GUIDANCE CORNER

| Home | About | Archive | Contact |

MONDAY, SEPTEMBER 23

Never Too Late

Today, I talked to a student who wanted to drop out. About one in four students don't graduate on time. Here's one story.

Rashida Harris inspires me. She shows us that it's never too late.

Advice and inspiration for Lincoln High School students

Search 🔍

Rashida's mother died when she was young. Rashida and her siblings moved in with an aunt.

Rashida's aunt did not value education. That attitude affected Rashida.

At school, Rashida fought with teachers. She did not study. "School wasn't that important to me," she says.

Instead, Rashida valued street life. Most days, she skipped school. She hung out with friends.

Often, they got into trouble. Nobody seemed to care.

At 16, Rashida dropped out. Then, she became a teen mom. She began to worry about **employment**.

WORDS TO KNOW!

attitude: a way of thinking or feeling

Academic Discussion

Key Idea

Q: What is the key idea of this part of the blog post?

A: The key idea is _____.

Rashida _____ school.

Important Details

Q: What happened in Rashida's life?

A: _____, Rashida _____.

1. Before dropping out:

2. After dropping out:

Summarize

Explain what led Rashida to drop out. Include the key idea and important details.

📖 **Text-Based Questioning**

Comprehension

Why did Rashida Harris go back to high school?

Rashida went back to high school because she _____

_____

_____

_____

_____

🔍 **Word Analysis**

(Circle) the S.M.A.R.T. words with two sounds. Underline the words with three sounds.

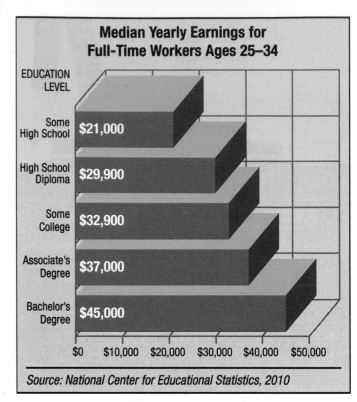

Median Yearly Earnings for Full-Time Workers Ages 25–34

EDUCATION LEVEL

- Some High School: $21,000
- High School Diploma: $29,900
- Some College: $32,900
- Associate's Degree: $37,000
- Bachelor's Degree: $45,000

$0 $10,000 $20,000 $30,000 $40,000 $50,000

Source: National Center for Educational Statistics, 2010

Check this out! High school graduates make about $9,000 more per year than dropouts.

Rashida wanted to be a role model for her daughter. She wanted a career. But she had no job skills.

"I've realized how much it's very important to receive an education," she says.

At 19, Rashida went back to school. This time, she is determined to graduate.

Then she will go to college. "Nowadays, [even] a high school diploma can't really get you a good job," she says.

Next, Rashida **will** return to the streets. But this time she will be a homicide detective!

She will investigate deaths. Rashida will solve crimes. Once she **succeeds**, she will be the role model she wants to be.

Resource Links:

- 📖 <u>Applying to College</u>
- 📖 <u>Why Staying in School Pays Off</u>
- 📖 <u>Dropout Prevention Programs</u>
- 📖 <u>Salary Calculator</u>

POSTED BY TYSON WALKER AT 9.13 AM

Leave a Comment

[   ] **Your Name**

[   ] **Your Email**

[   ] **Your Website**

[   ]

☐ Subscribe to this comment thread

WORDS TO KNOW!

career: work that offers chances for growth and progress

homicide: murder

Word Count 225   Lexile 370L

Academic Discussion

Key Idea

Q: What is the key idea of this part of the blog post?

A: The key idea is _____.

> Rashida _____ to graduate and has plans for a career.

Important Details

Q: What are Rashida's goals?

A: Rashida's goal for _____ is _____.

> 1. School:
>
>
> 2. A career:

Summarize

Explain how Rashida is changing her life. Include the key idea and important details.

Stretch Text

Turn to page 188 to read poetry about earning an alternative diploma.

Segmenting Words Into Sounds

How do you spell your name?

It's J-O-N. Jon.

Jon

Segment, or break, a word into its sounds.

Blend the sounds together to read the word.

Count It

Read each word. Count the number of sounds in each word. Write the number on the line.

1. am _____   **3.** it _____   **5.** yes _____

2. hat _____   **4.** trim _____   **6.** back _____

Segment It

Break each word into its sounds. Write each sound in a box.

1. an ☐☐

2. sun ☐☐☐

3. pot ☐☐☐

4. went ☐☐☐☐

5. if ☐☐

6. shop ☐☐☐

Sort It

Write the words with two sounds and the words with three sounds in the correct box.

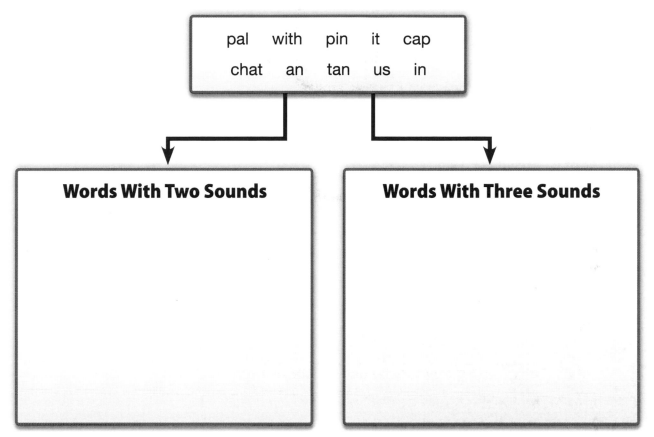

| | pal | with | pin | it | cap |
| | chat | an | tan | us | in |

Words With Two Sounds

Words With Three Sounds

Segment and Spell

Write the letters of the words you hear read aloud. Then write the word in the sentence.

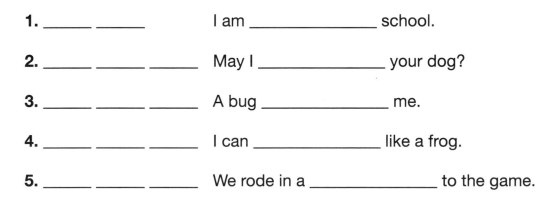

1. _____ _____   I am _____ school.

2. _____ _____ _____   May I _____ your dog?

3. _____ _____ _____   A bug _____ me.

4. _____ _____ _____   I can _____ like a frog.

5. _____ _____ _____   We rode in a _____ to the game.

Write an Argument

Prompt *How can schools help dropouts return to school?*

Prewrite

Review Text 3 on pages 22–25. <u>Underline</u> reasons Rashida dropped out of high school. Star reasons she went back. Write down two examples from the text.

My Notes

Text Evidence	In My Own Words
"Rashida's aunt did not value education. That attitude affected Rashida."	Her aunt didn't care about school. Rashida began to feel the same.

Academic Discussion

Take turns asking and answering questions with a partner.

Q: What is one reason Rashida dropped out of school?

A: One reason Rashida dropped out is that _____.

Q: What is one reason she went back?

A: One reason she went back is that _____.

Read an example of present-tense verbs. Then use your notes and the writing frame to answer the prompt.

Present-Tense Verbs

A present-tense verb describes action that is happening now or is ongoing.

Schools ___*prepare*___ students for jobs.
    (present-tense verb)

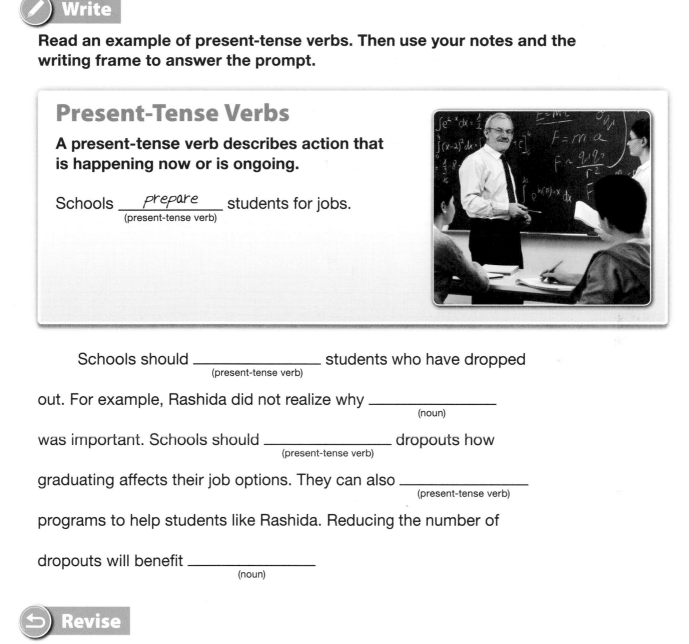

Schools should _____ students who have dropped
                (present-tense verb)

out. For example, Rashida did not realize why _____
                                                    (noun)

was important. Schools should _____ dropouts how
                                (present-tense verb)

graduating affects their job options. They can also _____
                                                        (present-tense verb)

programs to help students like Rashida. Reducing the number of

dropouts will benefit _____
                            (noun)

Revise

Read your writing and check your spelling. Make sure your responses are present-tense verbs or nouns.

Write an Application Essay

Practice writing a college essay. Write about an experience, story, or achievement that is important to you.

GATHER INFORMATION Look back at the texts. Write about what colleges are looking for.

A. _____

_____

B. _____

_____

BRAINSTORM Use the chart to come up with two ideas for your essay. Then choose the best one.

Experience, Story, or Achievement	Details	What It Tells Colleges About You

WRITE YOUR ESSAY Use the writing frame to complete your essay.

One experience that has impacted my life is _____

_____

_____

First, I _____

_____

_____

_____

In the end, _____

_____

_____

_____

This experience has affected me by _____

_____

_____

_____

I will succeed in college because _____

_____

_____

_____

✓ Self Check

Put a check mark in the box if you can answer "yes" to the following question.

❑ Did you include details that show why the experience or achievement was important?

PRESENT YOUR ESSAY Read your application essay to the group. Use a public voice.

SPECIAL FORCES

What does it take to belong to special forces?

Special forces take on exciting missions. For example, Navy SEALs killed Osama bin Laden. How do these soldiers train for their roles?

TEXT 1 Magazine Article

THE NAVY'S ELITE FORCES

To become Navy SEALs, soldiers must survive months of brutal training.

TEXT 2 Photographs

Read Primary Sources

See Navy SEALs in action.

TEXT 3 News Article

Hunt for bin Laden Ends

Read about how an elite team of soldiers killed the terrorist leader.

Anchor Word List

depended

gear

mission

specialty

wounded

Watch the video and complete the outline.

I. Soldier dogs are not like other soldiers. Their ___*specialty*___ is sniffing out bombs and bombers.

   A. A dog named Cairo was part of the _____ that killed Osama bin Laden.

   B. These dogs have special _____ such as vests with two-way radios and goggles.

II. Dogs like Lex, and the people who care for them, have _____ on one another to get through tight situations and to keep each other safe.

III. Lex was _____ and earned a special medal called the Purple Heart.

◔ **Discuss & Write**

Take turns asking and answering questions.

Q: What kinds of dangers do soldier dogs face?

A: Soldier dogs face danger when they _____

_____

_____

_____

Q: What is the relationship between dogs and their handlers?

A: The relationship between dogs and their handlers is _____ because

_____

_____

_____

_____

Build Word Knowledge

Target Word Read and rate each Target Word.*	Meaning Complete the Target Word meanings.	Examples Finish the Target Word examples below.
elite e•lite (adjective) p. 36 1 2 3 4	made up of the _____ people in a particular group	• _____ are an **elite** group of people. • To make an **elite** soccer team, you must _____
military mil•i•tar•y (noun) p. 46 1 2 3 4	the _____ who fight for a country	• _____ is one branch of the U.S. **military**. • If you join the **military**, you might learn to _____
training train•ing (noun) p. 36 1 2 3 4	the _____ needed to do a job or task	• You need **training** to _____ _____ • Learning to _____ is part of drivers' **training**.

STUDENT DRIVER

* Rating Scale   1 = I don't know it at all.   3 = I think I know the word.
                 2 = I've seen it or heard it.   4 = I know it and use it.

Word Families

Complete the meaning and examples for the Target Words.

training

Target Word	Meaning	Examples
train *train* *(verb)* p. 36	to _____ someone how to do something	• I could **train** someone to _____ _____ • Parents usually **train** their children to _____ _____

Target Word	Meaning	Examples
trained *trained* *(adjective)* p. 36	taught to _____ something well	• I would like to become a **trained** _____ _____ • A **trained** chef knows how to _____ _____

Target Word	Meaning	Examples
trainee *train•ee* *(noun)* p. 36	someone who is being _____ to do a job	• As a **trainee**, I would make sure to _____ _____ • When doctors are **trainees**, they learn _____ _____

Text-Based Questioning

Comprehension

What is one quality someone needs to become a Navy SEAL?

To become a Navy SEAL, someone must be

_____

_____

_____

_____

Word Analysis

(Circle) the S.M.A.R.T. words with short vowel sounds. Underline the words with long vowel sounds.

THE NAVY'S ELITE FORCES

Navy SEALs train for dangerous missions.

by Sonja Colvin

SEAL stands for Sea, Air, and Land. U.S. Navy SEALs are **trained** to work everywhere. They are the Navy's **elite** Special Operations forces.

To become a SEAL, you **must** be physically fit. You must be mentally tough.

SEALs endure months of brutal **training**. **Trainees** run hundreds of miles. They spend hours in icy water. They swim hard. They **dive** deep. They **scale** mountains. They jump from planes.

Only 30 percent **train** successfully. The **rest** drop out.

Requirements to enter SEAL training:

Exercise	Number or Distance	Time Limit
Swim	500 yards	12.5 minutes
Push-ups	42	2 minutes
Sit-ups	50	2 minutes
Pull-ups	6	none
Run in boots and long pants	1.5 miles	11.5 minutes

Those who **make** it perform dangerous missions. They spy on enemies. They raid enemy targets. They fight terrorists.

SEALs get great satisfaction from their work. They take great risks. However, they are proud to be elite warriors.

WORDS TO KNOW!

endure: to live through something hard

brutal: hard and painful

Word Count 113   Lexile 380L

Academic Discussion

Key Idea

Q: What is the key idea of the article?

A: The key idea of the article is _____.

Becoming a Navy SEAL

is _____

Important Details

Q: What do Navy SEALs do?

A: Navy SEALs do _____ that (is/are) _____.

1. Training:

2. Missions:

Summarize

Explain what it takes to become a Navy SEAL. Include the key idea and important details.

Stretch Text

Turn to page 189 to read a memoir about one Navy SEAL's training.

Contrasting Long and Short Vowels

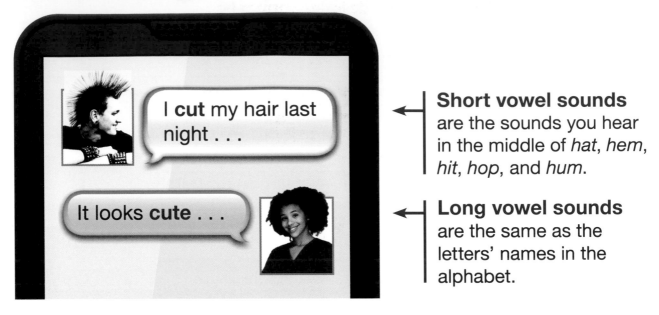

Short vowel sounds are the sounds you hear in the middle of *hat, hem, hit, hop,* and *hum.*

Long vowel sounds are the same as the letters' names in the alphabet.

Long Vowel Sounds

Write the letter of the long vowel sound you hear read aloud.

1. s ☐ m e
2. ☐ v e
3. m ☐ n e
4. h ☐ m e
5. m ☐ t e
6. ☐ c e

Short Vowel Sounds

Write the letter of the short vowel sound you hear read aloud.

1. b ☐ t
2. l ☐ d
3. h ☐ t
4. l ☐ t
5. r ☐ n
6. ☐ t

Long and Short Vowel Sounds

Circle the words with short vowel sounds. <u>Underline</u> the words with long vowel sounds.

| hid | hide | cod | code |
| huge | hug | mad | made |

Practice

Write the short and long vowel words in the correct box.

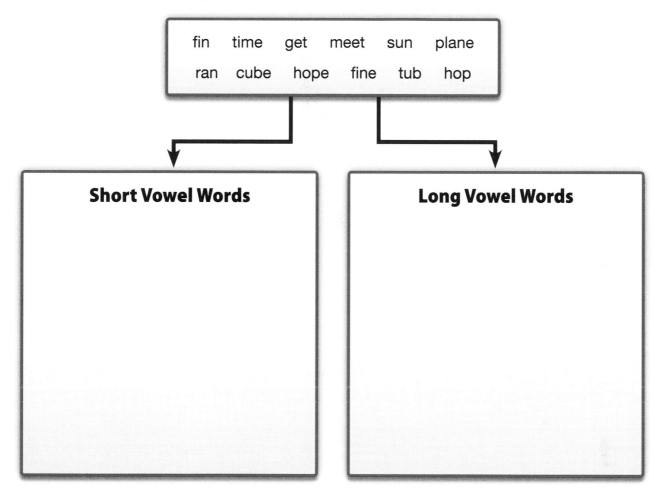

| fin | time | get | meet | sun | plane |
| ran | cube | hope | fine | tub | hop |

Short Vowel Words

Long Vowel Words

Context Clues

Write the correct word in the blank.

1. I _____ an apple. (at, ate)

2. I stayed _____ my cousin's house. (at, ate)

3. I had a _____ in my jeans. (rip, ripe)

4. The fruit was _____ (rip, ripe)

5. I took a bath in the _____ (tub, tube)

6. Air moved through the _____ (tub, tube)

Write an Informative Paragraph

Prompt | *What does it take to be a Navy SEAL?*

Prewrite

Review Text 1 on pages 36–37. ★Star at least two challenges Navy SEALs must meet. Write down two examples from the text.

My Notes

Text Evidence	In My Own Words
"SEAL stands for Sea, Air, and Land. U.S. Navy SEALs are trained to work everywhere."	SEALs work in multiple environments.

Academic Discussion

Take turns asking and answering questions with a partner.

Q: What is one challenge Navy SEALs face?

A: One challenge Navy SEALs face is _____.

Q: What is one quality Navy SEALs need?

A: One quality Navy SEALs need is _____.

Write

Read examples of adjectives. Then use your notes and the writing frame to answer the prompt.

Adjectives

An adjective describes something or someone. Adjectives can also tell how many or how much.

Navy SEALs are ___*special*___ forces.
                    (adjective)

The United States military has __*five*__ branches.
                                  (adjective)

_____ must be tough. They have to survive
        (noun)

months of _____ training. These elite _____
              (adjective)   (noun)

learn to work in multiple environments. To make it, SEALs must

be _____ and _____ Their training prepares
      (adjective)   (adjective)

them for _____ and _____ missions.
              (adjective)   (adjective)

Revise

Read your writing and check your spelling. Make sure your responses are adjectives or nouns.

Read Primary Sources

Navy SEALs are trained to work in the sea, in the air, and on land. Check out these SEALs in action. What has the photographer **captured**? What **camouflage** do they use?

Build Word Knowledge

Target Word Read and rate each Target Word.*	Meaning Complete the Target Word meanings.
capture *cap•ture* *(verb)* 1 2 3 4	to _____ or record
camouflage *cam•ou•flage* *(noun)* 1 2 3 4	clothing and materials that help people _____ in with their surroundings

* Rating Scale	1 = I don't know it at all. 2 = I've seen it or heard it.	3 = I think I know the word. 4 = I know it and use it.

Analyze

Use the photographs to answer the questions.

1. In the first photo, what has the photographer captured?

   The photographer captured the SEALs _____
   to work on a boat.

2. In the bottom photo, what kind of camouflage are the SEALs wearing?

   They are wearing _____

   _____

3. What do these photographs tell you about SEALs' training?

   From the photographs, I can tell that SEALs' training _____

   _____

Text-Based Questioning

Comprehension

Why does the author include the sentence "This story began on September 11, 2001"?

The author includes this sentence to

_____

_____

_____

_____

Word Analysis

Circle the S.M.A.R.T. words that are singular possessives. Underline the plural possessives.

TOWN TRIBUNE **NATIONAL**

Hunt for bin Laden Ends

By WENDELL REDDICK

WASHINGTON—Osama bin Laden is dead. U.S. special forces killed the terrorist leader.

Commandos landed in Pakistan. They raided **bin Laden's** hideout. They shot bin Laden. He was our **nation's** enemy.

Day of Terror

This story began on September 11, 2001. Terrorists attacked the United States.

They hijacked four jets. They flew three jets into buildings. The fourth jet crashed in a field.

Commandos landed in Pakistan. They raided bin Laden's hideout.

Who planned the attacks? Leaders needed to know. They had to stop the enemy from attacking again.

The government learned that Al Qaeda was responsible. It is a terrorist group. Bin Laden was the **group's** leader. He planned the attacks. Al Qaeda killed nearly 3,000 Americans.

The United States searched for bin Laden. He hid very well. He avoided capture for almost ten years. Thanks to the Navy SEALs' efforts, he is dead.

Navy SEALs killed Osama bin Laden. He died on May 2, 2011.

WORDS TO KNOW!

commandos: soldiers trained to carry out raids

hijacked: took control of a plane or vehicle by force

Academic Discussion

Key Idea

Q: What is the key idea of this part of the article?

A: The key idea is _____.

Navy SEALs _____ Osama bin Laden.

Important Details

Q: What happened on May 2, 2011, and September 11, 2001?

A: On _____, _____.

1. May 2, 2011:

2. September 11, 2001:

Summarize

Explain what happened before the commandos killed bin Laden. Include the key idea and important details.

📖 Text-Based Questioning

Comprehension

Why did the Navy SEALs use quiet helicopters?

The SEALs used quiet helicopters so that

_____

_____

_____

_____

🔍 Word Analysis

Circle the S.M.A.R.T. words that are singular possessives. Underline the plural possessives.

President Obama and his team gathered at the White House. They watched live updates.

Discovered at Last

In August 2010, the CIA made a discovery. They found a messenger. He worked for bin Laden.

The CIA spied on the man. He led them to our enemy's hideout.

For months, the CIA gathered information. The **military** made plans. Leaders planned a raid.

On April 29, President Barack Obama gave orders. Bin Laden must be assassinated!

Mission Accomplished

Two days later, 25 commandos gathered. They jumped into quiet helicopters. They raced to Pakistan. They landed at the hideout.

Two dozen commandos stormed inside. They belonged to SEAL Team 6. It is the elite of the elite. They carry out the most dangerous missions.

In 38 minutes, the Americans' mission was over. Bin Laden was dead. The SEALs achieved the military's goal.

Bin Laden was living in Abbottabad, Pakistan.

WORDS TO KNOW!

CIA: Central Intelligence Agency, a government group that gathers information about U.S. enemies

assassinated: killed in a surprise attack

Word Count 261   Lexile 390L

Academic Discussion

Key Idea

Q: What is the key idea of this part of the article?

A: The key idea is _____.

After nine years, the CIA _____ bin Laden and the military assassinated him.

Important Details

Q: How did the United States find and kill bin Laden?

A: During _____, the United States _____.

1. The search:

2. The mission:

Summarize

Explain what happened after the 9/11 attacks. Include the key idea and important details.

Stretch Text

Turn to page 189 to read another news article about the bin Laden mission.

Recognizing and Using Possessives

This is Mike's ball.

This mark (**'**) is an **apostrophe**. It shows ownership.

He can slam dunk two balls.

Do not confuse possessives with **plural nouns**. Plural nouns have an *s* at the end, but no apostrophe.

Write Possessives

Rewrite each sentence using a possessive noun.

1. The fur of the cat is black. _The cat's fur is black._

2. The cover of the book is red. _____

3. The bowl of the dog is empty. _____

4. The home of Kim is huge. _____

5. The pants of the man are red. _____

6. These are the bikes of Jose. _____

Contrast Singular and Plural Possessives

If a noun is **plural**, the possessive ends with an apostrophe after the letter *s*.

one baseball player's autograph

many baseball players' autographs

Practice

(Circle) the singular possessive nouns. Underline the plural possessive nouns.

cat's collar	maps	dogs' bowls	students' pens
fans' cheers	pin's message	lines	home's door

Revise Sentences

Rewrite each sentence using a singular or plural possessive noun.

1. These are the hats of the team. _These are the team's hats._

2. The shirt of my sister is green. _____

3. This is the food of the birds. _____

4. The sons of Brad are tall. _____

5. The horns of the cars are loud. _____

6. The room of my brothers is big. _____

Write an Argument

Prompt | *Why was the hunt for Osama bin Laden a key mission?*

Prewrite

Review Text 3 on pages 44–47. <u>Underline</u> details that describe bin Laden's crimes against the United States. Write down two examples from the text.

My Notes

Text Evidence	In My Own Words
"The government learned that Al Qaeda was responsible. It is a terrorist group. Bin Laden was the group's leader."	Bin Laden led the group that attacked the United States.

Academic Discussion

Take turns asking and answering questions with a partner.

Q: What did bin Laden do against the United States?

A: Bin Laden _____.

Q: How did the United States respond?

A: The United States responded by _____.

Write

Read examples of past-tense verbs. Then use your notes and the writing frame to answer the prompt.

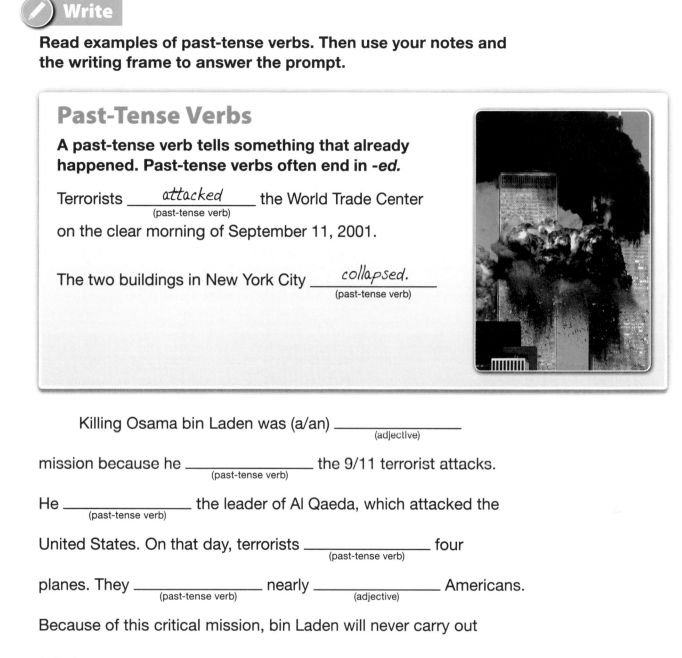

Past-Tense Verbs

A past-tense verb tells something that already happened. Past-tense verbs often end in -ed.

Terrorists _____*attacked*_____ the World Trade Center
 (past-tense verb)
on the clear morning of September 11, 2001.

The two buildings in New York City _____*collapsed.*_____
 (past-tense verb)

Killing Osama bin Laden was (a/an) _____
 (adjective)

mission because he _____ the 9/11 terrorist attacks.
 (past-tense verb)

He _____ the leader of Al Qaeda, which attacked the
 (past-tense verb)

United States. On that day, terrorists _____ four
 (past-tense verb)

planes. They _____ nearly _____ Americans.
 (past-tense verb) (adjective)

Because of this critical mission, bin Laden will never carry out

(a/an) _____ plot again.
 (adjective)

Revise

Read your writing and check your spelling. Make sure your responses are past-tense verbs or adjectives.

Give a Speech

Write a speech about special forces. Explain why these soldiers are important.

BRAINSTORM IDEAS Look back at the texts and other sources. Write two ways special forces protect the United States.

A. _____

_____

B. _____

_____

GATHER EVIDENCE For each idea, find supporting details in the text.

Who	What They Do	Why It Is Important

WRITE YOUR SPEECH Explain why special forces are important.

Special forces are an important part of the United States military. One way that they protect the United States is by _____

_____

_____

_____

_____

For example, they _____

_____

_____

_____

_____

Another way special forces have benefited the United States is by ____

_____

_____

_____

_____

_____

PRESENT YOUR SPEECH Give your speech to the group. Make eye contact with the audience.

✓ **Self Check**

Place a check mark in the box if you can answer "yes" to the following question.

☐ Did you use evidence from the text to support your claims?

MODULE 3

GAME ON!

6789

What is the science behind video games?

Making video games isn't just fun and games. Game developers must understand science and problem solving. On the other side, players can use games to make scientific discoveries!

TEXT 1 Magazine Article

SCIENCE AT PLAY

Physics plays an important role in games such as *Angry Birds*.

TEXT 2 Video Game Sketch

Read Primary Sources

Video game designers use sketches to create new games.

TEXT 3 News Article

Gaming for Good

A medical question stumped scientists for years. Gamers solved it in 10 days!

Anchor Understanding

Anchor Word List

determines

distributes

earns

launched

poverty

Watch the video and complete the outline.

I. A kid who plays the video game *Freerice* _____earns_____ rice instead of points.

II. The number of points _____ how much rice gets shipped to the people who need it.

   A. The rice is shipped to people who are hungry and live in extreme _____

III. *Freerice* _____ bags of rice to hungry people all over the world.

   A. *Freerice* has given out a lot of rice—97 billion grains—since it _____ in 2007.

Discuss & Write

Take turns asking and answering questions.

Q: How does playing *Freerice* help people who are hungry?

A: Playing *Freerice* helps people who are hungry by _____

_____

_____

_____

Q: How is *Freerice* different from many other video games?

A: *Freerice* is different from many other video games because _____

_____

_____

_____

Build Word Knowledge

Target Word	Meaning	Examples
Read and rate each Target Word.*	**Complete the Target Word meanings.**	**Finish the Target Word examples below.**
demonstrate *dem•on•strate* *(verb)* p. 67 1 2 3 4 	to show how something _____	• A new student might ask (a/an) _____ to **demonstrate** how the whiteboard works. • I could **demonstrate** how to _____ _____
design *de•sign* *(verb)* p. 68 1 2 3 4 	to _____ how something will look and work	• _____ **design** items as part of their jobs. • **Designing** (a/an) _____ _____ could be fun.
force *force* *(noun)* p. 58 1 2 3 4 	the strength or _____ to affect how an object moves	• I can use the **force** of my body to _____ _____ • The **force** of the _____ _____ knocked down a building.

* Rating Scale

1 = I don't know it at all.   **3** = I think I know the word.

2 = I've seen it or heard it.   **4** = I know it and use it.

Word Families

Complete the meaning and examples for the Target Words.

Target Word	Meaning	Example
design *de•sign* *(noun)* p. 67	the _____ and function of something	• I like the **design** of _____ _____ • A car's **design** might make it _____ _____ _____

design

Target Word	Meaning	Example
designer *de•sign•er* *(noun)* p. 59	someone who _____ how something will look and work	• If I were a **designer**, I would want to work on _____ • To be a good **designer**, someone needs to _____ _____

Text-Based Questioning

Comprehension

1. What do designers need to know to make games realistic?

   To make games realistic, designers need

   _____

   _____

   _____

   _____

2. How can physics make a bird's flight seem real?

   Physics can make a bird's flight seem real

   because _____

   _____

   _____

   _____

   _____

Vocabulary & Language

3. What does the word *strike* mean in paragraph 2?

   Strike means _____

Word Analysis

Circle the S.M.A.R.T. words with the same vowel sound as *but*. Underline the words with the same vowel sound as *bit*.

PHYSICS: LAWS OF MOTION

Gravity pulls the object down. This makes it follow a curved path.

The force of a slingshot pushes an object into the air.

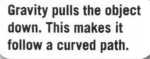

SCIENCE AT PLAY

Discover the Science Behind *Angry Birds*

by Giancarlo Molina

Angry Birds is a popular video game. Players use a slingshot. They launch birds into the air.

Sometimes, players aim well. Birds smash into a wall. They strike **just** the right spot. The **force** of the crash knocks down the wall. The wall crushes mean pigs.

Adjusting the angle of the sling affects how far the object travels.

Sometimes, players aim poorly. Then, the wall stands. Maybe the bird sails over it.

Designers want to make games realistic and **fun**. That means they **must** understand the laws of physics. They make objects in games move like they would in real life.

How high, fast, and far **will** each bird go? The answer depends on the laws of motion. Moving objects stay in motion, until forces such as gravity stop them.

How hard will the bird **hit** a wall? Will the wall fall? Did the player aim well? The physics of collisions can explain!

WORDS TO KNOW!

physics: the science that deals with energy, motion, and force

collisions: crashes when moving objects smash into other objects

Word Count 141   Lexile 450L

Academic Discussion

Key Idea

Q: What is the key idea of the article?

A: The key idea of the article is _____.

_____

use physics to make games like *Angry Birds* realistic.

Important Details

Q: How does physics affect parts of the game?

A: In the _____, physics affects _____.

1. Flight:

2. Collision:

Summarize

Explain how physics was important in creating *Angry Birds*. Include the key idea and important details.

Stretch Text

Turn to page 190 to read nonfiction about another video game design challenge.

Contrasting Short Vowels

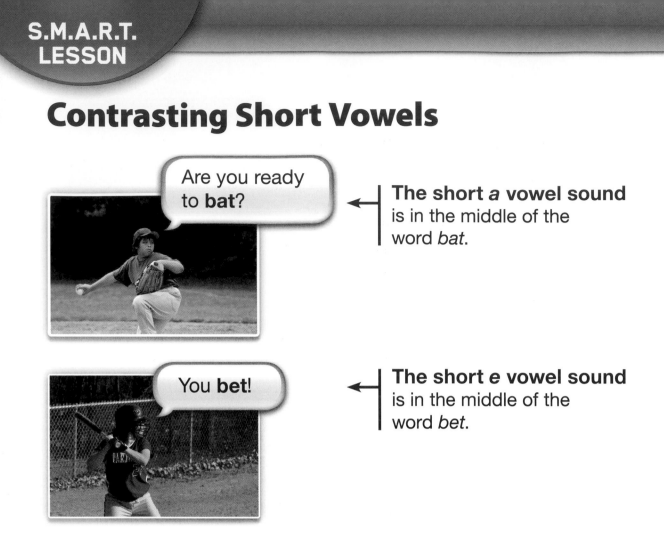

Are you ready to **bat**?

← **The short *a* vowel sound** is in the middle of the word *bat*.

You **bet**!

← **The short *e* vowel sound** is in the middle of the word *bet*.

Short Vowel Sounds

Write the letter of the short vowel sound you hear read aloud.

1. n ☐ t

2. n ☐ t

3. m ☐ p

4. m ☐ p

5. b ☐ g

6. b ☐ g

7. f l ☐ p

8. f l ☐ p

9. b ☐ n k

10. b ☐ n k

11. d ☐ s k

12. d ☐ s k

Identify Short Vowels

Read each word. <u>Underline</u> the letter that stands for the vowel sound.

red	rip	dog	fill	truck
cap	bug	map	stop	spin

Sort It

Write the short vowel words in the correct box.

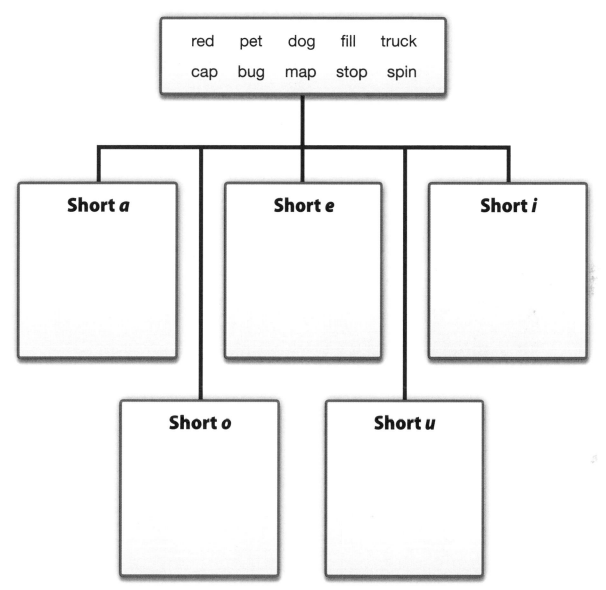

| red | pet | dog | fill | truck |
| cap | bug | map | stop | spin |

Short *a*

Short *e*

Short *i*

Short *o*

Short *u*

Context Clues

Write the correct word in the blank.

1. Can I _____ your dog? (pet/pot)

2. The kids will _____ in the sand. (dog/dig)

3. Take a ride in the _____ (truck/track)

4. I drank a _____ of milk. (cup/cap)

5. The dish _____ off the shelf. (fill/fell)

Write an Informative Paragraph

Prompt | *How did designers use physics to create* Angry Birds?

Prewrite

Review Text 1 on pages 58–59. ★Star at least three ways designers used physics. Write down three examples from the text.

My Notes

Text Evidence	In My Own Words
"The force of the crash knocks down the wall."	The birds have to hit walls to make them fall.

Academic Discussion

Take turns asking and answering questions with a partner.

Q: What is one way designers used physics?

A: Designers used physics to _____.

Q: What is another way physics was helpful?

A: Physics also helped designers figure out _____.

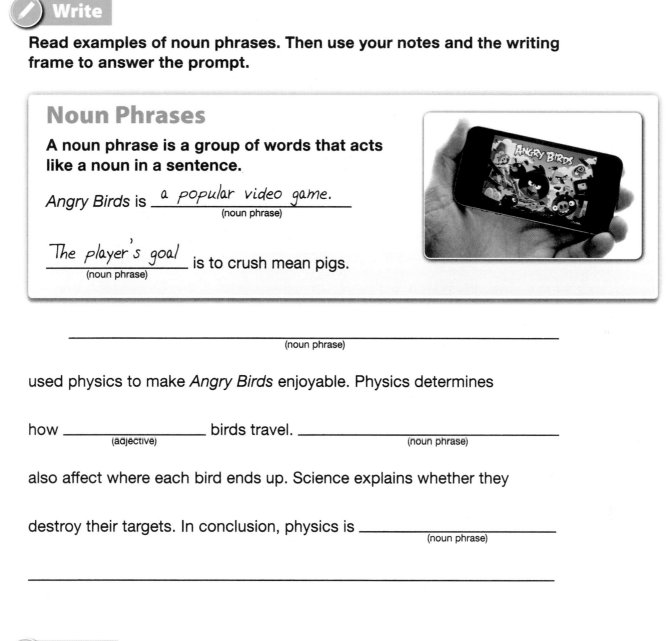

Write

Read examples of noun phrases. Then use your notes and the writing frame to answer the prompt.

Noun Phrases

A noun phrase is a group of words that acts like a noun in a sentence.

Angry Birds is _a popular video game._
(noun phrase)

The player's goal is to crush mean pigs.
(noun phrase)

_____
(noun phrase)

used physics to make *Angry Birds* enjoyable. Physics determines

how _____ birds travel. _____
(adjective)   (noun phrase)

also affect where each bird ends up. Science explains whether they

destroy their targets. In conclusion, physics is _____
(noun phrase)

_____

Revise

Read your writing and check your spelling. Make sure your responses are noun phrases or adjectives.

Read Primary Sources

To make video games, designers start with **sketches**. They create one for each **screen** of the game. Check out this screen from a game called *Sushi Monster*. Two companies, Houghton Mifflin Harcourt and Blockdot, worked together to create this app.

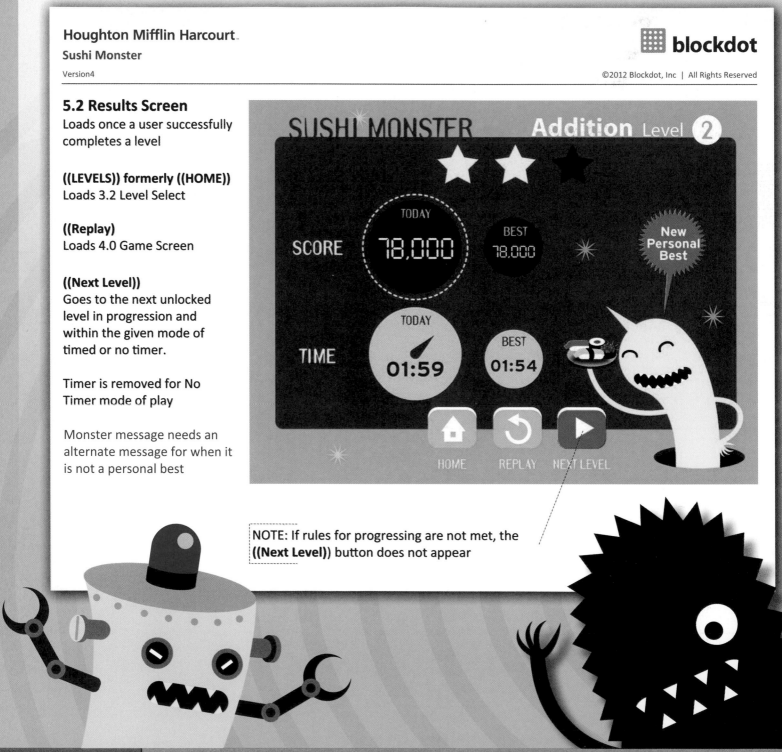

Houghton Mifflin Harcourt.
Sushi Monster
Version4

blockdot

©2012 Blockdot, Inc | All Rights Reserved

5.2 Results Screen
Loads once a user successfully completes a level

((LEVELS)) formerly ((HOME))
Loads 3.2 Level Select

((Replay)
Loads 4.0 Game Screen

((Next Level))
Goes to the next unlocked level in progression and within the given mode of timed or no timer.

Timer is removed for No Timer mode of play

Monster message needs an alternate message for when it is not a personal best

SUSHI MONSTER   Addition Level ②

SCORE   TODAY 78,000   BEST 78,000   New Personal Best

TIME   TODAY 01:59   BEST 01:54

HOME   REPLAY   NEXT LEVEL

NOTE: If rules for progressing are not met, the **((Next Level))** button does not appear

Build Word Knowledge

Target Word Read and rate each Target Word.*	Meaning Complete the Target Word meanings.
sketch *sketch* *(noun)* `1` `2` `3` `4`	a rough _____
screen *screen* *(noun)* `1` `2` `3` `4`	a still _____ from a game

* Rating Scale

`1` = I don't know it at all.   `3` = I think I know the word.
`2` = I've seen it or heard it.   `4` = I know it and use it.

Analyze

Use the sketch to answer the questions.

1. How does a player get to this screen of *Sushi Monster*?

   A player gets to this screen by _____

2. What text next to the sketch appears in red?

   The text that appears in red is _____

   _____

3. Why might this text be red?

   This text might be red because _____

   _____

4. How does this sketch help designers create the app?

   The sketch helps designers create the app because _____

   _____

Text-Based Questioning

Comprehension

1. What did researchers need to figure out?

   Researchers needed to figure out _____

   _____

   _____

   _____

   _____

   _____

2. Why did researchers want to solve this problem?

   Researchers wanted to solve this problem

   so that _____

   _____

   _____

   _____

   _____

Vocabulary & Language

3. What is an antonym of the word *activates* in paragraph 4?

   An antonym of *activates* is _____

   _____

Word Analysis

(Circle) the S.M.A.R.T. words that end with /t/. Underline words that end with /n/.

TOWN TRIBUNE **TECHNOLOGY**

Gaming for Good

By CARMEN SALAMANCA

In 10 days, gamers solved an important problem. They wanted to find out how a monkey virus worked.

A virus is a tiny particle. It infects living cells. It copies itself inside cells.

Some viruses cause deadly diseases. In humans, HIV causes AIDS. A similar virus causes AIDS in monkeys.

A Puzzling Protein

Viruses need proteins to reproduce. A **protein** activates the monkey virus. Researchers wanted to unlock the protein's structure. **That** might let them disable the protein.

At last, the researchers asked for help. They contacted video game players!

Proteins are long chains. They **twist** and **turn**.

Researchers studied the monkey virus protein. They worked on it for 10 years. Still, the protein puzzled them. They could **not** unlock its structure.

At last, the researchers asked for help. They contacted video game players!

The gamers play *FoldIt*. It is a science game. The game's **design** allows players to unlock proteins. They use animated 3-D models. They "fold" the models into shapes. Each folded model **demonstrates** a protein's structure.

Gamers played a science game called *FoldIt*.

Academic Discussion

Key Idea

Q: What is the key idea of this part of the article?

A: The key idea is _____.

Gamers _____ a problem related to a monkey virus.

Important Details

Q: Why are the virus and the protein important?

A: The _____ is important because it _____.

1. Virus:

2. Protein:

Summarize

Explain the researchers' attempt to find the shape of the protein. Include the key idea and important details.

📖 Text-Based Questioning

Comprehension

1. What do players do in *FoldIt*?

   In *FoldIt*, players _____

   _____

   _____

   _____

   _____

2. How will the gamers' success help scientists?

   The gamers' success will help scientists

   because _____

   _____

   _____

   _____

   _____

Vocabulary & Language

3. How did gamers show their ingenuity?

   Gamers showed their ingenuity by

   _____

   _____

   _____

🔍 Word Analysis

Circle the S.M.A.R.T. words that end with /d/. Underline words that end with /p/.

TOWN TRIBUNE **TECHNOLOGY**

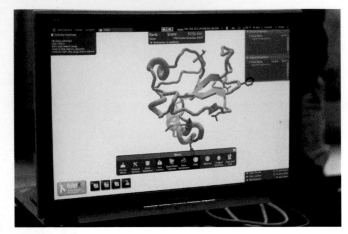

Gamers fold proteins into more stable shapes.

Gamers to the Rescue

Most *FoldIt* players are not scientists. They just love puzzles. Players use the game to find a protein's most stable shape. People are better at this than computers!

In 2011, *FoldIt* players went to work. They tried to unlock the monkey virus protein. They **designed** models. Then they tested each model. Had they folded the protein correctly?

"The ingenuity of game players can be used to solve a wide range of scientific problems."

In just 10 days, gamers **did** it! They figured out the structure of the protein. They succeeded where scientists **had** failed.

Exciting News

This is great news for science. Now, scientists can look for ways to block the protein. They might **stop** it from activating the monkey virus. In time, they might **find** new ways to treat human HIV!

"The ingenuity of game players . . . can be used to solve a wide range of scientific problems," one scientist said. Scientists are excited. They are happy to have gamers **help** them.

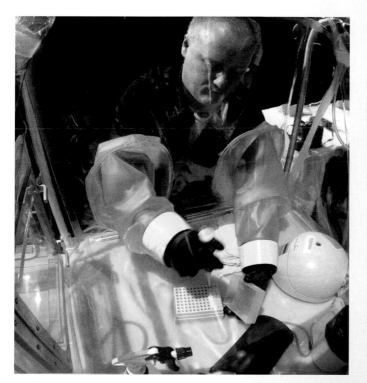

Scientists hope the discovery might help people.

WORDS TO KNOW!

models: copies of something that shows how it looks or works

ingenuity: cleverness

Word Count 310   Lexile 470L

Academic Discussion

Key Idea

Q: What is the key idea of this part of the article?

A: The key idea is _____.

> Scientists can use the gamers' discovery
> _____

Important Details

Q: How did gamers and scientists help others?

A: The _____ helped by _____.

1. Gamers:

2. Scientists:

Summarize

Explain how gamers solved the protein puzzle. Include the key idea and important details.

Stretch Text

Turn to page 190 to read a news article about a fitness game that helps others.

Contrasting Consonants

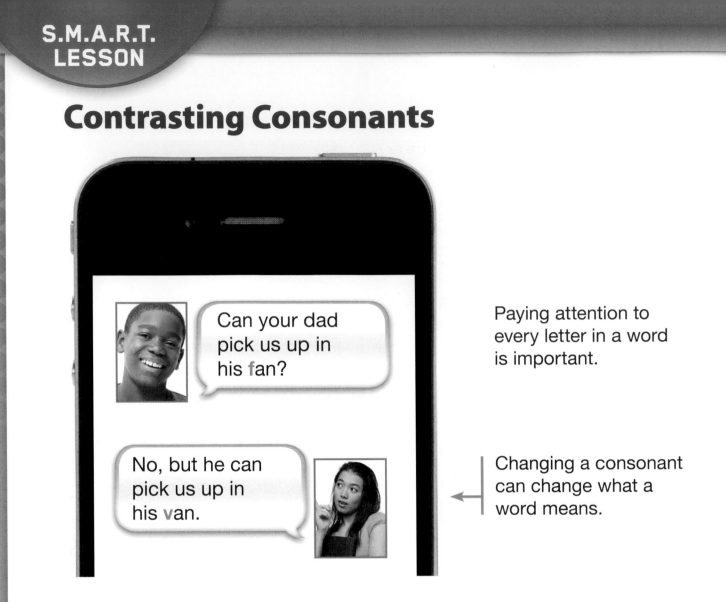

Can your dad pick us up in his **f**an?

No, but he can pick us up in his **v**an.

Paying attention to every letter in a word is important.

Changing a consonant can change what a word means.

Match It

(Circle) the word you hear read aloud. Listen for the initial consonant sounds.

1. pet	get	**3.** tin	bin	**5.** pot	got
2. mat	cat	**4.** jam	yam	**6.** nap	tap

Underline It

Underline the word you hear read aloud. Listen for the end consonant sounds.

1. peg	pet	**3.** hop	hot	**5.** bib	bid
2. rib	rid	**4.** ham	hat	**6.** bag	bad

Sentence Solver

Circle the word that completes the sentence.

1. I drank the hot cocoa from a _____. pug mug

2. The player put the basketball through the _____. net met

3. My dog likes to _____ a hole for his bones. big dig

4. There was a very _____ storm last night. bad dad

5. My friend screamed when he saw the big _____. bud bug

6. My uncle is the pilot of a _____. yet jet

7. The team rode to the game in a _____. van ran

8. Do you want a dog or a cat for a _____? get pet

Word Hunt

Use the words from the box to complete the sentences. You will not use every word.

rat	bib	lip	bid	ran	dog
peg	pen	lap	pot	jog	hot

1. The baby wore a _____

2. I write with a _____

3. The sun was very _____

4. To get exercise, I went for a _____

5. I held my new kitten in my _____

6. I hung my backpack on the _____

Write an Argument

Prompt	How should scientists and gamers work together?

Prewrite

Review Text 3 on pages 66–69. ★Star details that tell about the problem researchers faced and how they worked with gamers. Write down three examples from the text.

My Notes

Text Evidence	In My Own Words
"Researchers wanted to unlock the protein's structure. That might let them disable the protein."	Scientists tried to block the protein. They wanted to stop the monkey virus.

Academic Discussion

Take turns asking and answering questions with a partner.

Q: What problem did researchers face?

A: The problem researchers faced was _____.

Q: How did gamers help?

A: Gamers helped by _____.

Read examples of verb phrases. Then use your notes and the writing frame to answer the prompt.

Verb Phrases

A verb phrase is a group of words that shows an action or state of being.

A monkey virus *used a protein to copy itself.*
          (verb phrase)

Talented scientists *worked on the problem* for
          (verb phrase)

10 years.

Gamers should work with scientists _____
                    (verb phrase)

_____

For example, in 2011 scientists asked gamers for help with

_____
          (noun phrase)

In 10 days, the gamers _____
                    (verb phrase)

_____

Now, scientists can _____
                  (verb phrase)

_____

Therefore, more collaboration might lead to even more discoveries.

 **Revise**

Read your writing and check your spelling. Make sure your responses are noun or verb phrases.

Create a Slide Show

Give a presentation that explains how video games can be helpful.

GATHER INFORMATION Look back at the texts. Write about three ways games benefit people.

A. _____

_____

_____

B. _____

_____

_____

C. _____

_____

_____

ORGANIZE THE PRESENTATION Which examples do you want to share? Circle two examples.

PLAN Think about your slides and make notes. Each one should have:

- Information about how games are helpful
- An image from the Module (or other sources)

CREATE YOUR PRESENTATION Plan your slide show about how video games can be helpful.

Gaming Helps People

1. _____

_____

2. _____

_____

SLIDE 1

Benefit 1: _____

_____

_____

_____

In the image on page _____, you can see

_____

_____

_____

SLIDE 2

Benefit 2: _____

_____

_____

_____

In the image on page _____, you can see

_____

_____

_____

PRESENT YOUR SLIDE SHOW
Share your slide show with the group. Use an appropriate pace.

✓ Self Check

Place a check mark in the box if you can answer "yes" to the following question.

❏ Does each slide explain how video games can benefit people?

FAMOUS OR INFAMOUS?

How are TV and the Web affecting our culture?

More and more people seem to be finding fame through the Internet and reality TV. However, people often attract attention for unattractive behavior.

TEXT 1 Blog Post

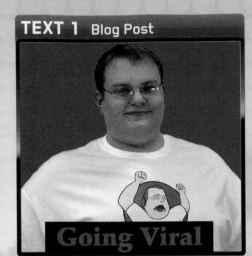

Going Viral

Is finding fame on the Internet worth it? Read about the experience of one "star."

TEXT 2 Editorial Cartoon

Read Primary Sources

A cartoonist offers his take on the reality TV craze.

TEXT 3 Op-Ed

Anything for Attention

Is reality TV bad for society? One writer weighs in.

Anchor Understanding

Watch the video and complete the outline.

I. Yiying Lu's drawing, *Fail Whale*, ended up on Twitter—

a ___*popular*___ website.

A. Twitter has a large _____ so many people saw
   Fail Whale.

II. Soon the artist, Yiying Lu, became _____ too.

A. Journalists _____ Yiying for newspapers, websites, radio, and TV.

III. Yiying decided to create other art to sell. She turned her Internet success into

a _____

Discuss & Write

Take turns asking and answering questions.

Q: How can becoming famous on the Internet benefit people? How can it be harmful?

A: Internet fame can benefit people _____

_____

_____

Internet fame can be harmful _____

_____

_____

Q: How did Yiying Lu benefit from becoming famous?

A: Yiying Lu benefited from becoming famous by _____

_____

_____

_____

Build Word Knowledge

Target Word Read and rate each Target Word.*	Meaning Complete the Target Word meanings.	Examples Finish the Target Word examples below.
considerable con•sid•er•a•ble *(adjective)* p. 81 1 2 3 4	large in _____ amount, or extent	• _____ (has/have) a **considerable** influence on teens' lives. • You would have to pay a **considerable** sum of money to _____ _____
culture cul•ture *(noun)* p. 88 1 2 3 4	the way of life of a nation or a group of _____	• Love of _____ is part of American **culture**. • A country's **culture** often includes traditional _____
media me•di•a *(noun)* p. 81 1 2 3 4	forms of mass _____ such as TV, radio, newspapers, and the Internet	• A form of **media** I use every day is _____ • One way I use **media** is _____ _____ _____

* Rating Scale
1 = I don't know it at all. **3** = I think I know the word.
2 = I've seen it or heard it. **4** = I know it and use it.

Word Families

Complete the meaning and examples for the Target Words.

Target Word	Meaning	Examples
cultural *cul•tur•al* *(adjective)* p. 88	related to the ideas, customs, and way of _____ of a group of people	• _____ can cause **cultural** changes. • A **cultural** idea many Americans share is a belief in _____

culture

Target Word	Meaning	Examples
uncultured *un•cul•tured* *(adjective)* p. 88	not having good manners or _____	• In my opinion, a TV show that features **uncultured** behavior is _____ _____ • At a restaurant, _____ _____ would be **uncultured**.

📖 Text-Based Questioning

Comprehension

1. How did Gary Brolsma become famous?

Gary Brolsma became famous by

_____

_____

_____

_____

2. Why did Brolsma find his fame embarrassing?

According to the text, he began to

_____

_____

so maybe he _____

_____

_____

Vocabulary & Language

3. Brolsma's video went "viral." How can an Internet video be like a virus?

An Internet video can be like a virus

because _____

_____

_____

🔍 Word Analysis

Circle the S.M.A.R.T. words that are contractions. Tell a partner what words were shortened.

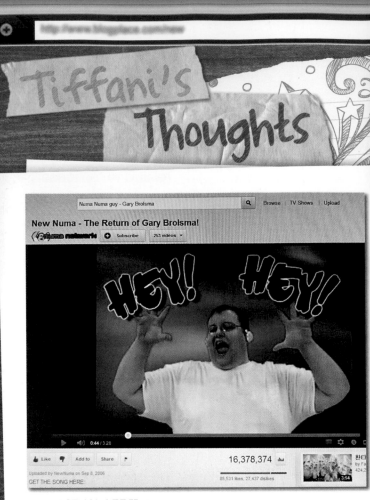

Tiffani's Thoughts

New Numa - The Return of Gary Brolsma!

16,378,374

THURSDAY, APRIL 25

Going Viral

On the Internet, almost anyone can become a star. Maybe I'll end up with millions of readers here!

But Internet fame can also be embarrassing! Just ask Gary Brolsma. In 2004, he was a regular teen from New Jersey. Brolsma worked at Staples. He enjoyed music in his spare time.

One day, Brolsma lip-synced to a pop song. The chorus sounds like "Numa Numa." He did a very silly dance, too. Brolsma shot a video of

CULTURE, MEDIA, AND OTHER RAMBLINGS

his performance. He posted the video online.

Brolsma **didn't** expect to attract a **considerable** number of viewers. But his video went viral. In time, it received 700 million hits! Suddenly, the "Numa Numa Guy" was in the **media**.

At first, he tried to enjoy his fame. He did interviews on TV talk shows. But soon, the attention became embarrassing.

Brolsma began to hide at home. "I want this to end," he told his grandmother.

That's another problem with Internet fame. It **won't** go away when you want it to. That silly dance could haunt you forever!

POSTED BY TIFFANI CARTER AT 7:05 PM

💬 Comment ✉ Share ★ Favorite

WORDS TO KNOW!

viral: fast spreading, like a virus

Word Count 172   Lexile 430L

Academic Discussion

Key Idea

Q: What is the key idea of the blog post?

A: The key idea of the blog post is _____.

An online video made Gary Brolsma famous, _____ was embarrassing.

Important Details

Q: How did Internet fame change Brolsma's life?

A: _____ the video went viral, Brolsma _____ .

1. Before:
2. After:

Summarize

Explain the downside of Internet fame. Include the key idea and important details.

Stretch Text

Turn to page 191 to read fiction about appearing in the media.

Recognizing and Using Contractions

Do not bother John's dog. It is asleep.

Don't bother Lisa's cat. It's asleep, too.

A **contraction** is formed by combining two words, with some letters left out. An apostrophe takes the place of the missing letters.

An apostrophe can also show possession. Do not confuse possessives with contractions.

Match It

Match each contraction with its word pair.

won't	didn't	he's	they'll	wasn't

1. he is _____

2. they will _____

3. was not _____

4. did not _____

5. will not _____

Write It

Read each contraction. Write the words that form the contraction.

1. hadn't _____

2. it's _____

3. doesn't _____

4. she's _____

5. they've _____

6. aren't _____

7. we'll _____

8. don't _____

9. they're _____

10. we're _____

Analyze Words

(Circle) each word with an apostrophe. Write *P* if it is a possessive and *C* if it is a contraction.

1. We haven't eaten dinner yet. _____

2. I lost my friend's computer. _____

3. You can't swim during a storm. _____

4. She's home sick today. _____

5. Our school's band won the contest. _____

6. I don't want to see that movie. _____

Use Contractions

Write a contraction in the blank to complete the sentences.

1. I _____ spread rumors. (will not)

2. _____ be here soon. (she will)

3. _____ go to the park. (let us)

4. I think _____ going on a trip. (he is)

5. I _____ know the answer. (do not)

6. _____ your brother? (Where is)

Write an Informative Paragraph

Prompt | *What was Gary Brolsma's experience with Internet fame?*

Prewrite

Review Text 1 on pages 80–81. ★Star the details that tell about Brolsma's experience. Write down three examples from the text.

My Notes

Text Evidence	In My Own Words
"In 2004, he was a regular teen from New Jersey."	Gary Brolsma lived a usual life.

Academic Discussion

Take turns asking and answering questions with a partner.

Q: How did Gary Brolsma become famous?

A: Brolsma became famous after he _____.

Q: How did Internet fame affect Brolsma?

A: Internet fame affected Brolsma by _____.

Read an example of conjunctions and phrases. Then use your notes and the writing frame to answer the prompt.

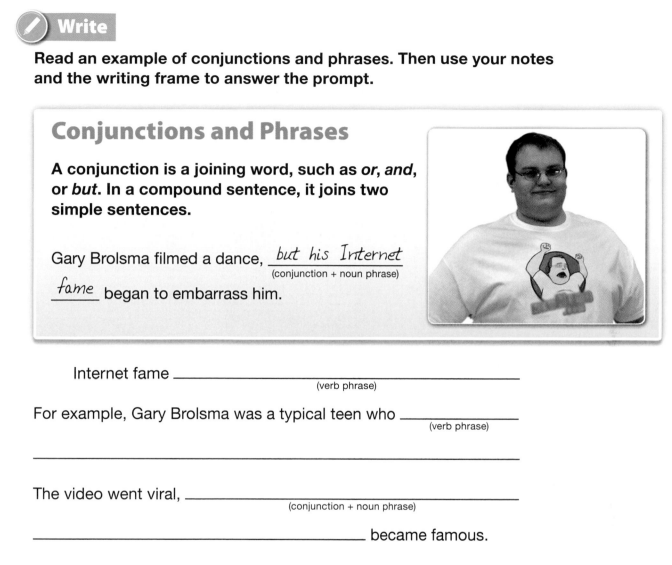

Conjunctions and Phrases

A conjunction is a joining word, such as *or*, *and*, or *but*. In a compound sentence, it joins two simple sentences.

Gary Brolsma filmed a dance, _but his Internet_
(conjunction + noun phrase)

fame began to embarrass him.

Internet fame _____
(verb phrase)

For example, Gary Brolsma was a typical teen who _____
(verb phrase)

_____

The video went viral, _____
(conjunction + noun phrase)

_____ became famous.

Soon, he began to feel embarrassed and hid at home. As

Brolsma's story shows, Internet fame may sound exciting,

_____
(conjunction + noun phrase)

can get out of control.

 **Revise**

Read your writing and check your spelling. Make sure your responses start with a verb or a conjunction.

Read Primary Sources

Editorial cartoons are **humorous** drawings with a serious purpose. These cartoons try to make readers laugh—and think. Here, artist Nick Anderson presents his opinion of reality TV.

Build Word Knowledge

Target Word Read and rate each Target Word.*	Meaning Complete the Target Word meanings.
humorous *hu•mor•ous* *(adjective)* [1] [2] [3] [4]	_____
infamy *in•fa•my* *(noun)* [1] [2] [3] [4]	fame from doing something _____

* Rating Scale

[1] = I don't know it at all. [3] = I think I know the word.
[2] = I've seen it or heard it. [4] = I know it and use it.

Analyze

Use the cartoon to answer the questions.

1. What is the man in the chair doing?

   He is _____

2. What do the people in the crowd want?

   They want _____

3. What are the people doing to achieve their goal?

   They are _____

4. Which statement best tells the message of this cartoon?

   A: Being on a reality TV show takes real talent.

   B: Being on a TV show is worth stepping on other people.

   C: People will do anything to get on a reality TV show.

   D: Filming a TV show is a good job to have.

📖 Text-Based Questioning

Comprehension

1. According to the author, what do most reality TV shows have in common?

The author claims that most reality TV

shows _____

_____

_____

_____

_____

2. How does the quote from Mark Andrejevic support the author's opinion?

The quote supports the author's opinion by

_____

_____

_____

_____

_____

Vocabulary & Language

3. What does "bread and butter" mean in paragraph 6?

"Bread and butter" means _____

_____

🔍 Word Analysis

Circle the S.M.A.R.T. words with two syllables. Underline the words with three syllables.

TOWN TRIBUNE **OPINION**

BY CLARKE ROBINSON

Anything for Attention

Reality TV is a **cultural** phenomenon! Reality shows pack TV schedules. How do these shows influence us? Are they damaging our **culture**?

A reality show stars real people. It does not star actors playing fictional characters.

Reality shows thrive on drama.

Reality shows fall into many categories. Some are competitions. People try to be the best singer or dancer. They try to win crazy **challenges**. Other shows focus on **problems**. Experts try to solve people's issues. Other shows just feature people's daily lives.

Almost all reality programs have something in **common**. They show people behaving badly. The stars scream and fight. They **gossip** and scheme. They cause trouble. Their behavior is **uncultured**!

Why? Reality shows thrive on drama. Bratty behavior grabs attention. The media discusses it. TV producers encourage reality stars to act out.

Mark Andrejevic is a college **professor**. He wrote a book about reality TV. "The bread and butter of reality television is to get people into a state where they are tired [and] stressed," he said.

Some reality TV shows are competitions. This one is for fashion designers.

WORDS TO KNOW!

phenomenon: remarkable person or thing

scheme: to plan to do something wrong

Academic Discussion

Key Idea

Q: What is the key idea of this part of the op-ed?

A: The key idea is _____.

_____

influence American culture, and they feature bad behavior.

Important Details

Q: How are reality TV shows different and similar?

A: One way reality TV shows are _____ is that they _____ .

1. Different:

2. Similar:

Summarize

Explain how reality TV shows attract viewers. Include the key idea and important details.

Text-Based Questioning

Comprehension

1. What evidence does the author include to support the idea that reality TV can "cause viewers to behave badly"?

   The author supports that idea with

   evidence that _____

   _____

   _____

   _____

2. What kind of reality shows does the author like?

   The author likes shows that _____

   _____

   _____

   _____

   _____

Vocabulary & Language

3. How does the suffix -*less* change the meaning of the word *talent* in paragraph 6?

   The suffix changes the meaning to

   _____

   _____

Word Analysis

Circle the S.M.A.R.T. words with two syllables. Underline the words with three syllables.

TOWN TRIBUNE **OPINION**

Stressed-out stars often fight. They tell secrets. They keep nothing private. Then they get more **airtime**. They become bigger stars.

Reality shows make bad behavior seem cool. This is bad news for American culture. These shows might cause viewers to behave badly, too.

In this show, chefs compete to see who is best.

One study suggests that this is true. Teens who watch reality TV accept more drama and **bullying** in their lives. Of teen girls who watch reality TV, 78 percent said gossiping is normal. Only 54 percent of those who don't watch much reality TV agreed.

Teens who watch reality TV accept more drama and bullying in their lives.

"When you're watching a TV show that implies that these are the real successful people, you're going to have to **mimic** these people," one expert said.

Reality TV can be okay. It can be entertaining. But shows should focus more on good **behavior**. They should feature exciting competitions.

Let's reward stars for talent and skill. Let's stop rewarding **talentless** brats.

WORDS TO KNOW!

implies: suggests without saying directly

mimic: to copy

Word Count 312   Lexile 530L

Academic Discussion

Key Idea

Q: What is the key idea of this part of the op-ed?

A: The key idea is _____.

> Many reality TV shows encourage
>
> _____
>
> but some feature skilled competitors.

Important Details

Q: What does the author like and dislike about reality TV shows?

A: The author _____ reality TV shows that _____.

> **1.** Likes:
>
>
> **2.** Dislikes:

Summarize

Explain how the author thinks reality TV should improve. Include the key idea and important details.

Stretch Text

Turn to page 191 to read a news article about the popularity of online videos.

Understanding Syllables

Cool!

A long word is easier to read if you split it into syllables.

A **syllable** has only one vowel sound—called a **vowel spot**. A vowel spot may be spelled with more than one vowel.

Groov / y!

Fan / tas / tic!

Identify Vowel Spots

Read each word. <u>Underline</u> each vowel spot in the word.

1. truck
2. limitless
3. robin
4. happen

5. plastic
6. habit
7. handful
8. cabinet

9. mess
10. dust
11. talentless
12. bonds

Sort Words

Write each word from the left page in the correct box.

One Syllable	Two Syllables	Three Syllables

Split It

Draw a line to divide each word into syllables. Then write the syllables.

1. pan|ic   _____pan_____   _____ic_____

2. traffic   _____   _____

3. upset   _____   _____

4. helpful   _____   _____

5. endless   _____   _____

6. napkin   _____   _____

7. sandwich   _____   _____

8. timid   _____   _____

Write an Argument

Prompt | *Does reality TV hurt our culture?*

📝 Prewrite

Review Text 3 on pages 88–91. ★Star details that tell how the author believes reality TV is harmful. Write down three examples from the text.

My Notes

Text Evidence	In My Own Words
"They show people behaving badly."	Negative behavior gets attention.

💬 Academic Discussion

Take turns asking and answering questions with a partner.

Q: What is a problem with reality TV?

A: A problem with reality TV is that _____.

Q: How does reality TV affect our culture?

A: Reality TV affects our culture by _____.

✏ Write

Read the examples of noun phrases. Then use your notes and the writing frame to answer the prompt.

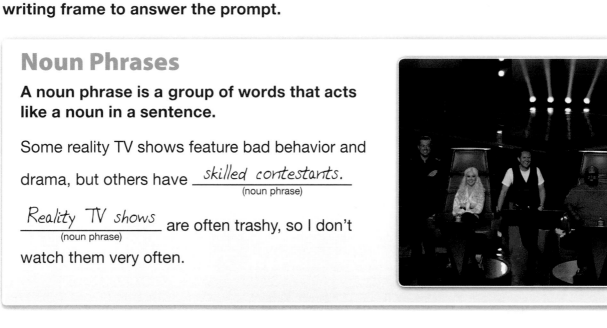

Noun Phrases

A noun phrase is a group of words that acts like a noun in a sentence.

Some reality TV shows feature bad behavior and

drama, but others have _skilled contestants._
(noun phrase)

Reality TV shows are often trashy, so I don't
(noun phrase)

watch them very often.

Reality TV shows can be entertaining, but many hurt our culture by

encouraging _____
(noun phrase)

On some shows, the stars have no talent, so they _____
(verb phrase)

_____

Reality TV shows make this behavior seem normal, as 78 percent of teen

girls said about _____
(noun phrase)

This form of media damages the whole culture, so shows should feature

_____
(noun phrase)

Think about what shows you decide to watch, and _____
(verb phrase)

_____

↺ Revise

Read your writing and check your spelling. Make sure your responses are noun or verb phrases.

Hold a Class Debate

Is reality TV benefiting us or harming us? Choose a position and argue it. Use text evidence to support your position.

EVALUATE EVIDENCE Look back at the texts. Write about two ways that reality TV affects our culture.

A. _____

_____

B. _____

_____

BRAINSTORM List the pros and cons of reality TV.

Pros	Cons

STATE YOUR POSITION Which side of the debate are you on?

Reality TV benefits/harms (circle one) viewers because _____

_____

TAKE NOTES Prepare for the debate. As each side argues its claims, record key ideas.

DEBATE: *Is reality TV benefiting us or harming us?*

OPENING STATEMENT: *Reality TV is* _____

_____

_____

OUR SIDE'S POSITION:	**POSSIBLE RESPONSE:**
A. _____	A. _____
_____	_____
_____	_____
B. _____	B. _____
_____	_____
_____	_____

SUMMARY/CLOSING STATEMENT: *In conclusion, reality TV is*

_____

_____

_____

✓ Self Check

Put a check mark in the box if you can answer "yes" to the following questions.

❑ Did you include evidence from the texts that supports your position?

❑ Did you address the other side's arguments?

FEAR FACTOR

Why do we love to be scared?

We pay money to be scared at movies, by books, and in haunted houses. Why are tales of horror so popular?

TEXT 1 Interview

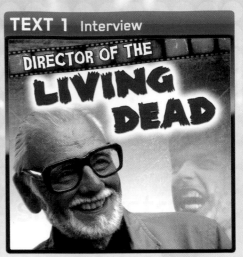

DIRECTOR OF THE LIVING DEAD

Meet George A. Romero, director of horror films like *Night of the Living Dead*.

TEXT 2 Diagram

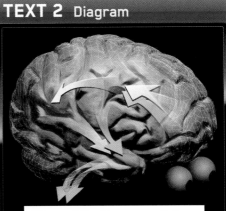

Read Infographics

This is your brain on . . . fear! Examine the brain activity that fear produces.

TEXT 3 Magazine Article

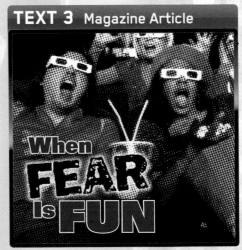

When FEAR is FUN

What are the most common fears? Does feeling afraid have benefits to our lives?

Anchor Understanding

Watch the video and complete the outline.

I. Alfred Hitchcock was an _____*authority*_____ on making people afraid.

    A. The films he directed are still _____ audiences today, even though he made them more than 50 years ago!

II. His ideas about creating fear were _____ But now, many people have followed his ideas.

III. Hitchcock's _____ for making people afraid included extreme close-ups, scary music, and putting the camera in the position of the person being chased so that audiences feel like they are being chased.

IV. _____ of filmmakers will continue to use his ideas to make scary movies.

Anchor Word List

authority
entertaining
generations
techniques
unique

Discuss & Write

Take turns asking and answering questions.

Q: Why was Alfred Hitchcock considered an authority on entertaining people through fear?

A: Hitchcock was considered an authority on entertaining people through fear because

_____

_____

_____

Q: How was Hitchcock's theory about making scary movies unique?

A: Hitchcock's theory about making scary movies was unique because _____

_____

_____

_____

Build Word Knowledge

Target Word Read and rate each Target Word.*	**Meaning** Complete the Target Word meanings.	**Examples** Finish the Target Word examples below.
emotion e•mo•tion (noun) p. 110 [1] [2] [3] [4]	a _____ such as happiness, sadness, anger, or fear	• An **emotion** I like to feel is _____ • I experience the **emotion** of fear when I _____ _____ _____
genre gen•re (noun) p. 102 [1] [2] [3] [4]	a _____ of books, movies, music, or art	• My favorite book or movie from the horror **genre** is _____ _____ _____ • My favorite **genre** of movies is _____
respond re•spond (verb) p. 112 [1] [2] [3] [4]	to _____	• I **respond** to most horror movies by _____ _____ • My teacher might **respond** with frustration if I _____ _____

* Rating Scale **1** = I don't know it at all. **3** = I think I know the word. **2** = I've seen it or heard it. **4** = I know it and use it.

Word Families

Complete the meaning and examples for the Target Words.

Target Word	Meaning	Examples
response *re•sponse* *(noun)* p. 112	an action or _____ caused by someone or something	• _____ is a common **response** to horror movies. • If someone were being bullied, my **response** would be _____ _____ _____

respond

Target Word	Meaning	Examples
responsive *re•spon•sive* *(adjective)* p. 112	_____ quickly and with interest	• I am always **responsive** to my friend's suggestion that we _____ _____ for fun. • People must be **responsive** if they want to become (a/an) _____ _____

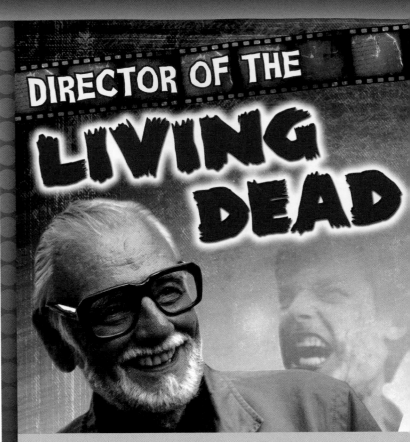

DIRECTOR OF THE LIVING DEAD

Text-Based Questioning

Comprehension

1. Do George A. Romero's movies focus on zombies as bad guys? Explain.

(Yes/No), Romero says that _____

_____

_____

_____

_____

2. Does Romero have rules for his zombies? Give examples.

(Yes/No), Romero says his zombies _____

_____

_____

_____

_____

Vocabulary & Language

3. What does the idiom "pointing the finger" mean in the first answer?

"Pointing the finger" means _____

_____

_____

Word Analysis

Circle the S.M.A.R.T. words that are compound words. Tell a partner the two words that make up each compound word.

In his lifetime, George A. Romero has directed films from many genres. He is most famous for zombie movies.

Q: **Are your zombies metaphors?**

A: To me, the zombies have always just been zombies. My stories are about humans and how they react, or fail to react, or react stupidly. I'm pointing the finger at us.

Q: **Why do zombies eat brains?**

A: I've never had a zombie eat a brain! I don't know where that comes from. Who says zombies eat brains?

Q: **But your zombies eat human flesh, right?**

A: Definitely.

Night of the Living Dead is one of Romero's most popular movies.

Q: **Your zombies cannot run. Modern zombies can. Why?**

A: I think it's video games, man. Zombies are always moving fast in video games. I still don't agree with it. If zombies are dead, how can they move fast? My guys don't run. They never have and they never will.

Q: **So, how do you survive a widespread zombie attack?**

A: Oh, boy. I don't know.

WORDS TO KNOW!

metaphors: things that serve as symbols of something else

flesh: skin, muscle, and fat

Word Count 149   Lexile 470L

Academic Discussion

Key Idea

Q: What is the key idea of the interview?

A: The key idea of the interview is _____.

> George A. Romero directs horror movies,
>
> and he _____
>
> _____

Important Details

Q: How does he describe his zombies?

A: His zombies' _____ is _____.

1. Purpose:

2. Diet:

3. Movement:

Summarize

Explain what Romero's zombies are like. Include the key idea and important details.

Stretch Text

Turn to page 192 to read fiction from the horror genre.

Recognizing and Using Compound Words

A **compound word** is formed from two smaller words.

Often, you can predict the meaning of a compound word from the meanings of its smaller words.

This paper tells the news. It is a newspaper.

Word List

Read the words. Then (circle) the compound words.

1. bedroom

2. admit

3. backpack

4. basket

5. sunset

6. daydream

7. unreal

8. rainbow

Split It

Draw a line between the two smaller words that form each compound word. Write the smaller words on the lines.

1. daylight _____ _____

2. doorknob _____ _____

3. eyesight _____ _____

4. birdcage _____ _____

5. treetop _____ _____

6. waterfall _____ _____

7. baseball _____ _____

8. hotdog _____ _____

Match It

Find the compound word that matches each meaning. Write the letter of the compound word on the line.

Compound Word

1. anthill _____
2. fingerprint _____
3. bookcase _____
4. toothbrush _____
5. headache _____

Meaning

a. a case for holding books

b. a hill that ants make

c. a print taken from a finger

d. a pain in your head

e. a brush to clean your teeth

Write It

Read the word list. Draw a line between the two smaller words that make up the compound word. Then use the words to fill in the sentence blanks.

| pancakes   firefighter   sunrise   homesick   loudspeaker |

1. My dog wakes up at _____

2. My father makes us _____ for breakfast every Saturday.

3. The fans heard "The Star-Spangled Banner" over a _____

4. When my brother went to sleep-away camp, he became _____

5. The people in the burning building were saved by a brave _____

Write an Informative Paragraph

Prompt *What are George A. Romero's rules for zombies?*

Prewrite

Review Text 1 on pages 102–103. ★ Star at least two details about George A. Romero's zombies. Write down two examples from the text.

My Notes

Text Evidence	In My Own Words
"To me, the zombies have always just been zombies. My stories are about humans and how they react, or fail to react, or react stupidly."	Romero focuses on people and their responses to zombies.

Academic Discussion

Take turns asking and answering questions with a partner.

Q: What are George A. Romero's movies really about?

A: Romero's movies are really about _____.

Q: How do Romero's zombies behave?

A: Romero's zombies _____.

Write

Read examples of verb phrases. Then use your notes and the writing frame to answer the prompt.

Verb Phrases

A verb phrase uses more than one word to describe an action.

In video games zombies *run after people,*
<u>(verb phrase)</u>

but in Romero's movies they *move slowly.*
<u>(verb phrase)</u>

George A. Romero _____

<u>(verb phrase)</u>

_____

but he says that his movies are really about people's responses.

Romero's zombies _____

<u>(verb phrase)</u>

_____

but many people think they eat brains. Romero _____

<u>(verb phrase)</u>

_____

and he says that his movies will always have _____

<u>(noun phrase)</u>

_____

Look out if you encounter a zombie because Romero has no _____

<u>(noun phrase)</u>

_____

 Revise

Read your writing and check your spelling. Make sure your responses are verb or noun phrases.

Read Infographics

When you are in serious danger, you need to respond fast! This diagram shows how the brain processes scary situations.

For example, you might see something long and thin in the grass. Your thalamus says it's a snake. You start to run away. Then, your **visual** cortex catches up. It provides detailed information about the danger to the rest of the brain. It tells you the snake is really just a stick.

2 The thalamus (in red) takes in **sensory** information. It relays it to other parts of the brain.

1 Information travels from the eyes to the thalamus to the amygdala along the blue path. Your brain begins responding to danger in only a few thousandths of a second.

5 The visual cortex is the yellow area. This part of the brain makes sense of what your eyes see.

3 The amygdala (in green) processes fear. It causes you to respond to threats and danger.

4 Information travels from the eyes to the thalamus, the visual cortex, and the amygdala along the yellow path. On this route, information takes more than twice as long to get to the amygdala.

Build Word Knowledge

Target Word Read and rate each Target Word.*	Meaning Complete the Target Word meanings.
visual *vis•u•al* *(adjective)* 1 2 3 4	related to _____
sensory *sen•so•ry* *(adjective)* 1 2 3 4	related to the five _____: sight, smell, touch, taste, and hearing

Analyze

Use the diagram to answer the questions.

1. How are the blue and yellow paths similar?

   In both paths, visual information goes from the eyes to the _____ and reaches the _____

2. How are the paths different?

   The paths are different because in the yellow one, information goes to the _____ before it goes to the amygdala.

3. What does the visual cortex do?

   The visual cortex _____

4. The blue path helps you react quickly, even if that snake is just a stick. Why would this be helpful?

   This would be helpful because _____

Text-Based Questioning

Comprehension

1. Does the author believe that people are easy to understand?

The author believes that people

_____ (are/are not) easy to understand. Evidence

that supports this is _____

_____

_____

_____

2. The article says that "we are wired to seek pleasure." Why does the author include this information?

The author includes this information

because it _____

_____

_____

_____

Vocabulary & Language

3. Which word in the text is an antonym for the word *negative* in paragraph 1?

_____ is an antonym

for *negative*.

Word Analysis

Circle the S.M.A.R.T. words with a stressed first syllable. Underline the words with a stressed last syllable.

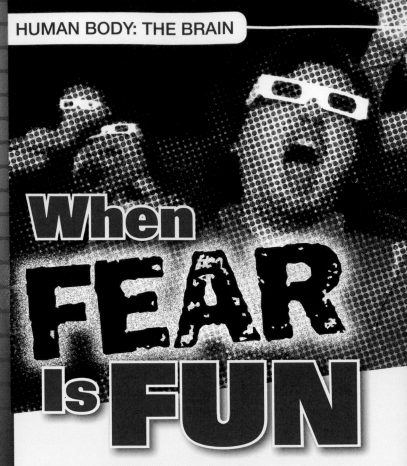

HUMAN BODY: THE BRAIN

When FEAR is FUN

by Lavell Posada

Why do people enjoy fear?

As **humans**, we want to feel good. We are wired to seek pleasure. We **avoid** pain and negative experiences. That is our nature, right?

Well, maybe we are more complicated than that. Fear is a **negative emotion**. Yet, many people love haunted houses. They love scary movies and books. They love the whole horror genre.

These people don't just seek scary experiences. They actually pay to be scared!

The audience screams at a 3-D horror movie.

FEAR SEEKERS

Why do people pursue scary experiences? Scientists offer several **possible** reasons. For one, maybe people don't really enjoy fear. But we do enjoy relief. Relief is a positive emotion—and we feel it when a scary experience ends.

Maybe some people endure fear just to enjoy the relief afterward. Many people also feel proud when they survive something scary.

Or maybe it's not really fear people feel in a haunted house. Maybe they actually feel excitement. Excitement, like relief, is positive. We enjoy the thrills in "thrills and chills."

WORDS TO KNOW!

endure: to put up with

Academic Discussion

Key Idea

Q: What is the key idea of this part of the article?

A: The key idea is _____.

Many humans enjoy the reaction _____ _____, and scientists have found many possible explanations.

Important Details

Q: How do fear and relief affect us?

A: _____ affects us by _____.

1. Fear:

2. Relief:

Summarize

Explain how some people enjoy being scared. Include the key idea and important details.

Text-Based Questioning

Comprehension

1. What are the physical responses to fear?

   The physical responses to fear include

   _____

   _____

   _____

   _____

2. Does the author believe people should try new experiences? What evidence supports this claim?

   The author (does/does not) believe that

   people should try new experiences.

   Evidence that supports this is that he says

   _____

   _____

   _____

   _____

Vocabulary & Language

3. In paragraph 1, the author says that some people enjoy the "rush of adrenaline." What does *rush* mean in this context?

   In this context, *rush* means _____

   _____

Word Analysis

Circle the S.M.A.R.T. words with a stressed first syllable. Underline the words with a stressed last syllable.

ADRENALINE RUSH

Some people enjoy the physical **response** to fear. When something scares you, your body **responds**. You experience a rush of adrenaline. This hormone makes your heart rate increase. Your **breathing** speeds up, too. Your muscles are also **responsive** because they tense up.

This **response** is called "fight or flight." It's useful when you're in real danger. The response helps you run away or stay and fight to protect yourself.

However, at a scary **movie**, you are safe. You don't need to run or fight. Yet, your body still produces adrenaline. Some people like this sensation; they enjoy the rush.

MIXED EMOTIONS

Our brain structure also plays a role in enjoying fear. The brain has areas called the amygdala and the nucleus accumbens. Both areas process pleasure. They both process fear, too. So maybe these emotions get confused!

Our love of fear might not be an accident. Humans probably benefit from the ability to **enjoy** fear. That's because it leads us to explore new experiences.

For example, making a new friend or trying a new sport can be scary. But they can also benefit us.

What would happen if fear were no fun? We might be scared to try anything new.

Structure of the Brain

The red dot shows the location of the nucleus accumbens. This area of the brain plays a role in pleasure. It also plays a role in fear.

The yellow dot shows the location of the amygdala. It also processes fear and pleasure.

WORDS TO KNOW!

hormone: a chemical that sends messages to parts of the body

benefit: to improve or help

Word Count 361 | Lexile 510L

Academic Discussion

Key Idea

Q: What is the key idea of this part of the article?

A: The key idea is _____.

The way our bodies and brains work might enable us to enjoy fear, and this can lead to an increase _____

Important Details

Q: How does fear affect us?

A: In the _____, fear _____.

1. Body:

2. Brain:

Summarize

Explain why we might enjoy fear and how it might help us. Include the key idea and important details.

Stretch Text

Turn to page 192 to read an article about another theory of why people enjoy fear.

Identifying Stressed and Unstressed Syllables

I'm so stressed out!

Why?

I have to find the stressed syllable in **finding**.

That's easy. Just remember: Endings like -*ed* and -*ing* are not stressed when you add them to words.

Every word with more than one syllable has a stressed syllable.

The stressed syllable gets the most emphasis when you say the word.

Mark It

Listen to and repeat each word. <u>Underline</u> the syllable that is stressed.

1. action

2. balloon

3. insect

4. monster

5. cucumber

6. kangaroo

Split It

Write each word in syllables. Then circle the stressed syllable.

1. expect _____

2. jumping _____

3. difficult _____

4. subtract _____

5. puzzle _____

6. vacation _____

Word List

Say each word aloud. <u>Underline</u> the syllable that is stressed.

contest   disgusted   asking

before   unlocked   table

banana   expecting   because

Sort It

Write each word from the list in the correct box.

First Syllable Stressed	Middle Syllable Stressed	Last Syllable Stressed
contest		

Word Hunt

Fill in the missing word in each sentence. Find the word in the list.

1. Our team came in second in the spelling _____ *contest.* _____

2. My mother was _____ when she saw my messy room.

3. When are they _____ us to arrive?

4. Look both ways _____ you cross a street.

5. After our meal, the _____ was full of dirty dishes.

6. A monkey likes a _____, and so do I.

Write an Informative Paragraph

Prompt | *Why do many people seek out scary experiences?*

Prewrite

Review Text 3 on pages 110–113. <u>Underline</u> details that describe possible
reasons people enjoy fear. Write down three examples from the text.

My Notes

Text Evidence	In My Own Words
"Many people love haunted houses. They love scary movies and books."	Scary experiences can include watching films, reading, and going to scary places.

Academic Discussion

Take turns asking and answering questions with a partner.

Q: What is one reason people enjoy scary experiences?

A: One reason people enjoy scary experiences is that _____.

Q: What is a benefit of fear being fun?

A: A benefit of fear being fun is _____.

✏️ Write

Read examples of prepositional phrases. Then use your notes and the writing frame to answer the prompt.

Prepositional Phrases

A prepositional phrase begins with a preposition, such as *at*, *in*, *from*, *to*, *with*, or *by*. Prepositional phrases show relationships.

Some people love going ___*to horror movies,*___
(prepositional phrase)

and they enjoy being scared ___*by suspenseful scenes.*___
(prepositional phrase)

Many people enjoy _____
(noun phrase)

even though fear is a negative emotion. Scientists think that one reason for this

could be that people enjoy the relief _____
(prepositional phrase)

People also might experience excitement instead, or they might enjoy the responses

_____
(prepositional phrase)

Another reason that fear can seem fun is that the brain processes fear and pleasure

_____
(prepositional phrase)

Whatever the reason, enjoying fear can be a benefit, and it can motivate people to

try _____
(noun phrase)

 **Revise**

Read your writing and check your spelling. Make sure your responses are prepositional phrases or noun phrases.

Prepare a Presentation

How does fear affect the brain? Create a presentation for other students.

CONSIDER YOUR AUDIENCE Brainstorm two ideas to get other students interested in the topic.

1. _____

   _____

2. _____

   _____

GATHER INFORMATION Review the texts and take notes on important information. Find an image for each brain response.

Brain Response	Details	Image(s)

COLLABORATE Break the presentation into parts. Decide who will present each part.

PLAN YOUR PRESENTATION Use the information you gathered to plan your presentation.

PRESENTATION TITLE: _____

GOALS: What do you want students to know after your presentation?

Students will _____

_____

MATERIALS: What items do you need?

Texts/Worksheets	
Visuals	
Websites/Technology	

PROCEDURE: Plan each part of your presentation.

1. Introduce the topic: _____

_____

_____

2. Present the key ideas: _____

_____

_____

_____

3. Wrap up your presentation: _____

_____

_____

Self Check

Put a check mark in the box if you can answer "yes" to the following questions.

❑ Did your introduction get the audience's attention?

❑ Did you use visuals to explain each key idea?

PRESENT YOUR PRESENTATION Share your presentation with the group. Use confident posture.

GUILTY
UNTIL PROVEN INNOCENT

Could our justice system be improved?

Stop-and-frisk policies affect many people who have done nothing wrong. Innocent people sometimes end up in jail. What can citizens do if our justice system gets it wrong?

TEXT 1 Op-Ed

Frisked for No Reason

One young man tells his story of multiple encounters with the police.

TEXT 2 Police Report

Read Primary Sources

U12-03302   CRIMINAL DAMAGE TO PROPERTY   72
              BATTERY   720-5/12-3
              BURGLARY RESIDENTIAL   720-5/19-3
              LOCATION: 300 BLOCK OF ELM ST E
              OCCURRED: 6/16/2012 12:00 REPORTED: 6/16/2(
              OFFICER: BUCKLEY, KURT M

SUMMARY: OFFENDER FORCED HIS WAY INTO RES
              DAMAGED PROPERTY OWNED BY VICTIM 3. O
              2 OF OWING HIM MONEY & STOLE VICTIM 2'S
              BATTERED VICTIM 1 WHILE INSIDE THE RESID

PROPERTY: DAMAGED   1 DOOR / FRAME

              STOLEN   1 CELLULAR PHONE

PEOPLE: VICTIM   AGE: 19 SEX: F URBANA   IL
             VICTIM   AGE: 19 SEX: M URBANA   IL

Examine a real-life police report from a burglary.

TEXT 3 Magazine Article

FIGHTING FOR JUSTICE

The Innocence Project has helped free hundreds of innocent people from prison.

Watch the video and complete the outline.

Anchor Word List

attorney
evidence
manager
microscopic
powerful

I. Betty Anne Waters believed in her brother. She went to law school and became an ___*attorney*___ so she could prove that her brother had not committed a crime.

   A. Betty Anne found _____ that showed that her brother did not commit the crime.

   B. She checked what she found for DNA—_____ material that only matches one person.

II. What Betty Anne found was _____ enough to get her brother a new trial. At the new trial, her brother was found innocent. Now he was free!

III. Betty Anne did not continue to work as an attorney. Now she is the _____ of a restaurant. Her job and her family make her happy.

✍ **Discuss & Write**

Take turns asking and answering questions.

Q: What did Betty Anne do to prove that her brother was innocent?

A: To prove that her brother was innocent, Betty Anne _____

_____

_____

_____

Q: Why didn't Betty Anne continue working as an attorney?

A: Betty Anne didn't continue working as an attorney because _____

_____

_____

_____

Build Word Knowledge

Target Word Read and rate each Target Word.*	Meaning Complete the Target Word meanings.	Examples Finish the Target Word examples below.
deny *de•ny* *(verb)* p. 132 ☐1 ☐2 ☐3 ☐4	to state that something is not _____	• The security guard accused the teens of _____ _____ but they **deny** it. • I **deny** that I have ever _____ _____
innocent *in•no•cent* *(adjective)* p. 133 ☐1 ☐2 ☐3 ☐4	not _____ of a crime	• _____ an **innocent** person is wrong. • The judge told the **innocent** man that _____ _____
justice *jus•tice* *(noun)* p. 133 ☐1 ☐2 ☐3 ☐4	_____ and reasonable treatment	• Many people value peace, **justice**, and _____ • You could go to _____ _____ for **justice** if someone wrongs you.

* **Rating Scale**
1 = I don't know it at all.   **3** = I think I know the word.
2 = I've seen it or heard it.   **4** = I know it and use it.

Word Families

Complete the meaning and examples for the Target Words.

Target Word	Meaning	Examples
denial de•ni•al (noun) p. 132	a statement that something is not _____	• I hope that _____ believe my **denial**. • Despite the athlete's **denial**, he faces _____ for cheating.

deny

Target Word	Meaning	Examples
undeniable un•de•ni•a•ble (adjective) p. 135	definitely _____	• My skill at _____ _____ is **undeniable**. • _____ _____ (has/had) an **undeniable** talent for leadership.

Text-Based Questioning

Comprehension

1. Describe the sequence of events in this op-ed.

   First, the author was frisked _____

   _____

   Next, he was frisked while _____

   _____

   Finally, he was frisked a third time as he

   _____

   _____

2. How have the author's feelings about the police changed?

   The author used to think the police were

   cool, but now he thinks _____

   _____

   _____

   _____

Vocabulary & Language

3. How does the prefix *un-* change the meaning of the word *fair* in paragraph 6?

   The prefix *un-* changes the meaning of *fair*

   to _____

Word Analysis

Circle the base word in each S.M.A.R.T. word. Then underline the prefix, suffix, or ending.

THE NEW YORK TIMES **OP-ED**

BY NICHOLAS K. PEART

Frisked for No Reason

One evening in August of 2006, I was celebrating my 18th birthday with my cousin and a friend. Suddenly, squad cars surrounded us. A policeman **yelled**, "Get on the ground!"

I was stunned. And I was scared. Then I was on the ground—with a gun pointed at me. I couldn't see what was **happening**. But I could feel a policeman's hand reach into my pocket and remove my wallet. **Apparently** he found the ID I kept there.

Then I was on the ground—with a gun pointed at me.

Less than two years later, N.Y.P.D. officers stopped and **frisked** me, again. This time I was leaving my grandmother's home.

I was stopped again in September of 2010. This time I was just walking home from the gym.

These experiences changed the way I felt about the police. After the third incident, I worried when police cars drove by.

When I was young I thought cops were cool. They had a **respectable** and honorable job. Now, I think their tactics are unfair. They abuse their authority.

Nicholas K. Peart is a college student in New York City. Police there have stopped almost 700,000 people in 2011.

WORDS TO KNOW!

tactics: ways of doing something

authority: the power to give orders

Word Count 164   Lexile 470L

Academic Discussion

Key Idea

Q: What is the key idea of the op-ed?

A: The key idea of the op-ed is _____.

> Nicholas K. Peart was stopped and frisked multiple times, and this changed his opinion
> _____

Important Details

Q: What did the police do each time they stopped Peart?

A: The _____ time, the police _____.

1. First:

2. Second:

3. Third:

Summarize

Describe the author's experiences. Include the key idea and important details.

Stretch Text

Turn to page 193 to read fiction about when "the wrong man went to prison."

Unlocking Multisyllable Words

I am **unlocking** this door.

I am **un-lock-ing** this word!

Long words are easier to read if you split them into parts. You can add word parts to **base words**.

Prefixes are word parts added to the beginning of base words to change their meaning.

Suffixes and **endings** are word parts added to the end of base words to change their meaning or part of speech.

Identify Base Words

Read each word. Then (circle) its base word.

1. handed	**5.** unpack	**9.** unlock	**13.** limited
2. frosting	**6.** limitless	**10.** unwell	**14.** handful
3. unlimited	**7.** defrosted	**11.** packing	**15.** unlocking
4. defrost	**8.** locked	**12.** wellness	**16.** unpacked

Analyze Word Parts

Complete the chart by breaking each word into parts. Some words may not have a prefix or a suffix/ending.

	Prefix	Base Word	Suffix/Ending
1. nonfiction	non	fiction	
2. preheating			
3. dislikable			
4. narrowest			
5. overcrowded			
6. unpack			
7. agreeable			
8. incorrectly			

Determine Meaning

Read each clue below. Then add a prefix, suffix, and/or ending to each base word to form a word that matches the clue.

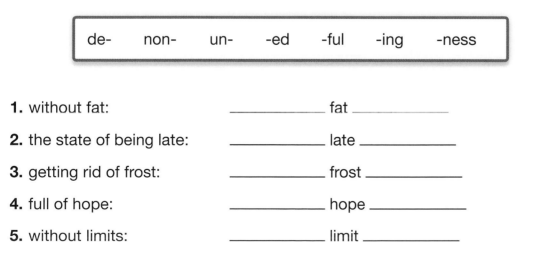

de-   non-   un-   -ed   -ful   -ing   -ness

1. without fat: _____ fat _____

2. the state of being late: _____ late _____

3. getting rid of frost: _____ frost _____

4. full of hope: _____ hope _____

5. without limits: _____ limit _____

Write an Informative Paragraph

Prompt | *How have Nicholas K. Peart's experiences affected his view of the police?*

Prewrite

Review Text 1 on pages 124–125. <u>Underline</u> details about the author's experiences with the police. Write down three examples from the text.

My Notes

Text Evidence	In My Own Words
"When I was young I thought cops were cool."	He used to look up to the police.

Academic Discussion

Take turns asking and answering questions with a partner.

Q: How did the police treat Nicholas K. Peart?

A: The police _____.

Q: Why did Peart's opinion of the police change?

A: Peart's opinion of the police changed because _____.

Read an example of prepositional phrases. Then use your notes and the writing frame to answer the prompt.

Prepositional Phrases

A prepositional phrase begins with a preposition, such as *at*, *in*, *from*, *to*, *with*, or *by*. Prepositional phrases show relationships.

Peart was stopped and frisked while walking

home _____*from the gym,*_____ but he had not done
(prepositional phrase)

anything wrong.

Nicholas K. Peart's experiences _____
(prepositional phrase)

_____ changed his attitude about the police.

In 2011, he was one of almost 700,000 people who were stopped

and frisked in New York City, and this _____
(verb phrase)

_____

As a child, Peart _____
(verb phrase)

_____

Then police stopped and frisked him multiple times _____
(prepositional phrase)

_____ and these encounters

affected his opinions. Because of these experiences, Peart thinks

the police do not treat people fairly, and he disagrees _____
(prepositional phrase)

_____

Read your writing and check your spelling. Make sure your responses start with a preposition or past-tense verb.

TEXT 2
Police Report

Read Primary Sources

After police respond to a call, they fill out a police report. News reporters often use police reports to share information with the public. What happened in this burglary? Think about what information is included.

U12-03302   CRIMINAL DAMAGE TO PROPERTY   720-5/21-1
            BATTERY   720-5/12-3
            BURGLARY RESIDENTIAL   720-5/19-3
            LOCATION: 300 BLOCK OF ELM ST E
            OCCURRED: 6/16/2012 12:00 REPORTED: 6/16/2012 12:27
            OFFICER: BUCKLEY, KURT M

SUMMARY: OFFENDER FORCED HIS WAY INTO RESIDENCE & IN THE PROCESS DAMAGED PROPERTY OWNED BY VICTIM 3. OFFENDER ACCUSED VICTIM 2 OF OWING HIM MONEY & STOLE VICTIM 2'S CELL PHONE. OFFENDER BATTERED VICTIM 1 WHILE INSIDE THE RESIDENCE.

PROPERTY: DAMAGED   1 DOOR / FRAME

        STOLEN   1 CELLULAR PHONE

PEOPLE: VICTIM   AGE: 19 SEX: F URBANA   IL
        VICTIM   AGE: 19 SEX: M URBANA   IL
        VICTIM   AGE: 55 SEX: M
        OFFENDER AGE: 44 SEX: M

Build Word Knowledge

Target Word Read and rate each Target Word.*	Meaning Complete the Target Word meanings.
offender of•fend•er (noun) [1] [2] [3] [4]	someone who commits a _____
batter bat•ter (verb) [1] [2] [3] [4]	to _____ someone

* Rating Scale	[1] = I don't know it at all. [2] = I've seen it or heard it.	[3] = I think I know the word. [4] = I know it and use it.

Analyze

Use the police report to answer the questions.

1. What are the three crimes the offender is charged with?

The offender is charged with _____

_____

2. Summarize what happened.

On June 16, _____

_____

3. Where did this happen?

This happened at _____

4. Why might the report not include the full address or names of the people involved?

The report might not include the full address or names to _____

_____

Text-Based Questioning

Comprehension

1. How is Travis Hayes's opinion of the police similar to or different from Nicholas K. Peart's in Text 1?

   Hayes and Peart have (similar/different)

   views of the police because _____

   _____

   _____

   _____

2. Does the author think the Innocence Project is a good organization?

   The author thinks the Innocence Project

   (is/is not) a good organization because

   _____

   _____

   _____

   _____

Vocabulary & Language

3. In the introductory text, what does "behind bars" mean?

   "Behind bars" means _____

   _____

Word Analysis

Circle the S.M.A.R.T. words that begin with open syllables. Underline the words that begin with closed syllables.

FIGHTING FOR JUSTICE

Thousands of innocent people are behind bars. The Innocence Project fights to free them.

by Sonia Patel

In April 1997, Ryan Matthews and Travis Hayes were seventeen years old. One day, the friends were driving down a local street. Suddenly, police officers stopped them. The teens were not surprised.

"Being a young black man in New Orleans, I saw people getting hassled by the police every day," Hayes said.

But this was no ordinary stop. A murder and robbery had taken place nearby. The getaway car looked like Hayes's car. Now, the teens became suspects.

Travis and Ryan denied any involvement. But police did not believe their denials.

Then, a witness wrongly identified Matthews as the murderer. Meanwhile, police pressured Hayes until he cracked. He confessed to driving the getaway car. Yet, Matthews and Hayes were totally **innocent**.

Criminal Injustice

In 1999, the young men went to prison. A few years later, the Innocence Project stepped in. This group was founded in 1992. Its members include lawyers and case analysts. They work to bring **justice** to innocent prisoners.

How do innocent people end up in prison? The Innocence Project has found several common problems.

WORDS TO KNOW!

pressured: tried to get someone to do something

confessed: admitted to doing something wrong

Academic Discussion

Key Idea

Q: What is the main idea of this part of the article?

A: The main idea is _____.

> Ryan Matthews and Travis Hayes went to prison _____
>
> _____

Important Details

Q: How did Matthews and Hayes end up in prison?

A: _____ reason Matthews and Hayes ended up in prison was that _____.

> **1.** One:
>
>
> **2.** Another:
>
>
> **3.** A third:

Summarize

Explain what happened to Ryan Matthews and Travis Hayes. Include the key idea and important details.

Text-Based Questioning

Comprehension

1. Does the author think that the criminal justice system needs improvement?

The author (does/does not) think the

justice system needs improvement

because _____

_____

_____

_____

2. How is DNA useful in solving crimes?

DNA is useful in solving crimes because it

_____

_____

_____

_____

Vocabulary & Language

3. How does the prefix *mis-* change the meaning of the word *use* in paragraph 6?

The prefix *mis-* changes the meaning of

use to _____

_____

Word Analysis

Circle the S.M.A.R.T. words that begin with open syllables. Underline the words that begin with closed syllables.

Matthews and Hayes's story is typical. For example, witnesses often make mistakes. They identify the wrong people. Sometimes, witnesses even lie.

Like Hayes, many suspects become scared or confused when police question them. They confess to crimes they did not commit.

In some cases, the justice system itself is the problem. Police and lawyers can make mistakes.

Fighting for Freedom

So far, the Innocence Project has helped to free almost 300 people.

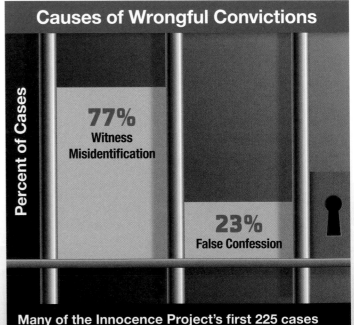

Causes of Wrongful Convictions

Percent of Cases

77%
Witness Misidentification

23%
False Confession

Many of the Innocence Project's first 225 cases involved problems with witnesses and confessions. Cases can have more than one problem.

The group takes on cases in which DNA evidence might prove a prisoner innocent.

What is DNA evidence? DNA is found in parts of the body such as blood and hair. Each person's DNA is unique. Often, criminals and **victims** leave DNA at crime scenes. This evidence shows who was there.

Sometimes, investigators ignore or misuse this evidence. Then, the Innocence Project works to have the evidence examined again.

In Matthews and Hayes's case, the murderer left a ski mask behind. The DNA didn't match either of theirs. When it was **finally** examined again in 2003, the evidence was **undeniable**. Matthews had not worn the mask. Another man—who had bragged about committing the crime—did.

Matthews spent seven years in prison, and Hayes spent 10 years. Finally, they were free.

WORDS TO KNOW!

typical: like many others

investigators: people who work to solve crimes

Word Count **380** | Lexile **580L**

Academic Discussion

Key Idea

Q: What is the main idea of this part of the article?

A: The main idea is _____.

> The Innocence Project helps prisoners get out of jail _____
>
> _____

Important Details

Q: How does the Innocence Project help people?

A: The Innocence Project (helps/helped) _____ by _____.

> **1.** Innocent prisoners:
>
>
>
> **2.** Matthews and Hayes:

Summarize

Explain how the Innocence Project helps people. Include the key idea and important details.

Stretch Text

Turn to page 193 to read a guidebook about citizens' rights.

Using Open and Closed Syllable Strategies

An open syllable ends in a vowel and usually has a long vowel sound.

LOCAL Foods

OPEN

A closed syllable ends in a consonant and usually has a short vowel sound.

FANTASTIC Fans

CLOSED

Open or Closed?

Underline the vowel spots in each word. Circle the words that begin with open syllables. Underline the words that begin with closed syllables.

1. h<u>o</u>tel

2. plastic

3. button

4. human

5. recent

6. public

7. napkin

8. jacket

9. basic

10. cricket

11. raven

12. travel

Analyze Words

Draw a line to divide each word into syllables. Write the syllables on the lines. (Circle) each open syllable.

1. dis|gust   _dis_   _gust_

2. silent   _____   _____

3. recent   _____   _____

4. constant   _____   _____

5. talent   _____   _____

6. focus   _____   _____

7. happen   _____   _____

8. label   _____   _____

Sentence Solver

Blend the syllables to read the words. Write the correct word in each blank.

plas tic	fu ture	traf fic
mu sic	blan ket	se cret

1. My new computer has a red _____ cover.

2. We were late because of _____

3. In the _____ I want to visit my grandparents.

4. I wear headphones when I listen to _____

5. Can you keep a _____

6. Bring a _____ in case it gets cold.

Write an Argument

Prompt | *Should the criminal justice system be improved?*

Prewrite

Review Text 3 on pages 132–135. <u>Underline</u> evidence that supports your claim.
Write down two examples from the text.

My Notes

Text Evidence	In My Own Words
"Like Hayes, many suspects become scared or confused when police question them. They confess to crimes they did not commit."	People sometimes make false confessions.

Academic Discussion

Take turns asking and answering questions with a partner.

Q: Should the criminal justice system be improved?

A: The justice system (should/should not) be improved because _____.

Q: How does the justice system affect people?

A: One way the justice system affects people is _____.

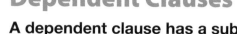 **Write**

Read an example of a dependent clause. Then use your notes and the writing frame to answer the prompt.

Dependent Clauses

A dependent clause has a subject and a verb but is not a complete sentence. They often start with words such as *because, when, after, before, although,* or *while.*

Although Travis Hayes was innocent,
<u>(dependent clause)</u>

he spent years in prison.

We (should/should not) improve the criminal justice system

_____
(dependent clause)
_____

For example, Ryan Matthews and Travis Hayes's case shows that people

_____
(verb phrase)
_____

Therefore, we should _____
(verb phrase)

_____

Another reason to (change/maintain) the justice system is to discourage

crime _____
(dependent clause)

_____

In conclusion, the criminal justice system _____
(verb phrase)

_____

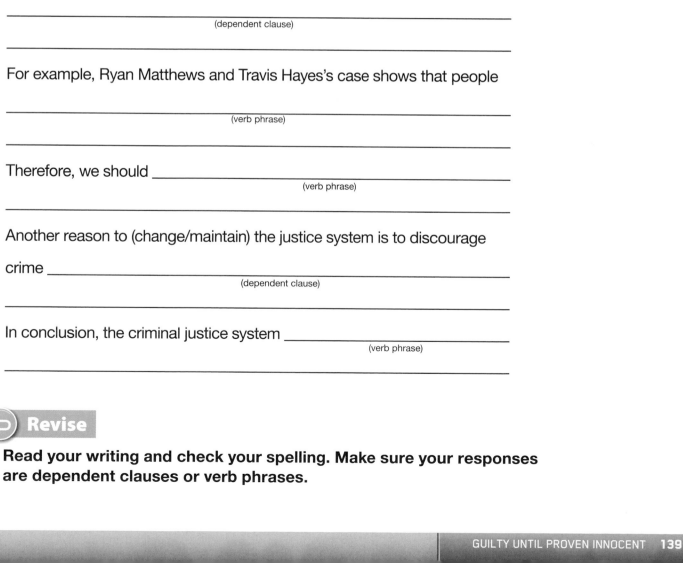

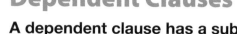 **Revise**

Read your writing and check your spelling. Make sure your responses are dependent clauses or verb phrases.

Create a Survey

How does law enforcement affect your community? Design a survey to find out.

GATHER INFORMATION Look back at the readings. What are some important issues related to our criminal justice system?

1. _____

2. _____

3. _____

ANALYZE QUESTION TYPES An effective survey asks the right kinds of questions. For each question type, come up with an example.

Question Type	Purpose	Example
Yes/No	They are useful for questions with only two options.	
Rating Scale	They are useful for times when people need more than two options.	
Open-Ended	They allow people to respond in their own words.	

WRITE YOUR SURVEY Create a four-question survey to find out about criminal justice in your community.

SURVEY TITLE: _____

1. _____

_____

_____

_____

2. _____

_____

_____

_____

3. _____

_____

_____

_____

4. _____

_____

_____

_____

✓ **Self Check**

Put a check mark in the box if you can answer "yes" to the following questions.

❏ Does your survey use at least two question types?

❏ Does your survey include space for people to answer each question?

PRESENT YOUR SURVEY Share your survey with the group. Use clear pronunciation.

LOSING THEIR MINDS?

How should coaches and teams protect players?

Concussions are common in contact sports like football and hockey. These brain injuries result from hits to the head. Now, science shows that they can cause serious, lasting health problems.

TEXT 1 Magazine Article

FOUL PLAY?

What are researchers discovering about concussions?

TEXT 2 Fact Sheet

HEADS×UP
CONCUSSION IN HIGH SCHOOL SPORTS

Read Primary Sources

Rules protect injured players and determine when they can play again.

TEXT 3 Op-Ed

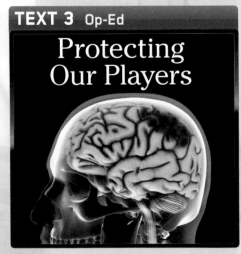

Protecting Our Players

A young player's death exposes the risks of contact sports.

Watch the video and complete the outline.

collide

concentrate

champions

fierce

severe

I. Girls who play soccer can be _____fierce_____ and fearless.

II. However, sometimes these girls _____ with each other during a game.

III. This can lead to injuries so _____ that the girls end up with concussions.

IV. These injuries make it difficult for the girls to _____ which makes it hard to do well in school.

V. Some soccer _____ believe that playing soccer is not dangerous as long as the players learn to play correctly.

✐ **Discuss & Write**

Take turns asking and answering questions.

Q: What are some of the harmful effects that might happen to girls when they play soccer?

A: Some harmful effects that might happen to girls when they play soccer are _____

_____

_____

_____

_____

Q: Why do some people say that girls should keep playing soccer?

A: Some people say that girls should keep playing soccer because _____

_____

_____

_____

Build Word Knowledge

Target Word Read and rate each Target Word.*	Meaning Complete the Target Word meanings.	Examples Finish the Target Word examples below.
athlete ath•lete *(noun)* p. 146 `1` `2` `3` `4`	someone who plays a _____	• _____ _____ is important to most **athletes**. • To be a good **athlete**, you need to _____ _____
medical med•i•cal *(adjective)* p. 146 `1` `2` `3` `4`	having to do with the treatment of _____ and illnesses	• _____ _____ is a **medical** problem. • To get help for a **medical** problem, you might go to _____ _____
research re•search *(verb)* p. 146 `1` `2` `3` `4`	to _____ a topic	• A topic I would like to **research** is _____ _____ • Scientists **research** the human body to discover _____ _____

* Rating Scale

1 = I don't know it at all.	**3** = I think I know the word.
2 = I've seen it or heard it.	**4** = I know it and use it.

Word Families

Complete the meaning and examples for the Target Words.

Target Word	Meaning	Examples
athletic *ath•let•ic* *(adjective)* p. 147	having to do with _____	• An **athletic** event I would like to see is _____ • An example of **athletic** equipment is _____

athlete

Target Word	Meaning	Examples
athletics *ath•let•ics* *(noun)* p. 147	physical games and _____	• One type of **athletics** at our school is _____ • Youth **athletics** can teach children _____ _____

Text-Based Questioning

Comprehension

1. Why should athletes heal from concussions before they return to sports?

_____

_____

_____

_____

_____

2. What is the purpose of the tests that Mater Dei football players take before and after concussions?

_____

_____

_____

_____

_____

Vocabulary & Language

3. How does the suffix –ly change the meaning of the adjective *serious* in paragraph 4?

_____

_____

_____

Word Analysis

Circle S.M.A.R.T. words with short vowel sounds in the first syllable. Underline words with long vowel sounds in the first syllable.

Dr. Ann McKee runs the VA CSTE Brain Bank. Here, she cuts apart a brain.

FOUL PLAY?

by Rickie Cruz

Concussions are brain injuries. They are common in contact sports. Many **athletes** with concussions play again before their brains heal. That can make the injury worse.

What happens to athletes who suffer multiple concussions? At Boston University, the VA CSTE Brain Bank **researches** this question. Scientists there study deceased athletes' brains.

The scientists are finding that most of these athletes had Chronic Traumatic Encephalopathy (CTE). **Medical** research shows that multiple hits to the head cause CTE. This fatal brain disease causes dementia.

Teams want to protect players from CTE. Mater Dei High School in California is famous for its football program. Its **athletic** department takes concussions seriously.

Before the season begins, every player takes thinking tests. After a concussion, the player takes the tests again. If the scores are lower, the concussion may be affecting his brain. He can't return to football until his scores are normal.

Players often try to hide injuries. "These kids want to fight through it," says trainer Mike Fernandez. So, coaches tell everyone to report teammates with possible concussions. Anyone who is hit on the head should get checked out.

Unfortunately, not every school is this careful. A 2009 study found that 40 percent of high schoolers with concussions returned to **athletics** too soon.

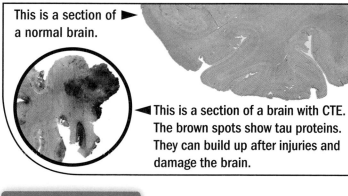

This is a section of ► a normal brain.

◄ This is a section of a brain with CTE. The brown spots show tau proteins. They can build up after injuries and damage the brain.

WORDS TO KNOW!

deceased: dead

dementia: a disorder that causes memory loss, confusion, and personality changes

Word Count 209   Lexile 690L

✍ Academic Discussion

Key Idea

Q: What is the key idea of the article?

A: The key idea of the article is _____.

_____

_____

_____

Important Details

Q: What are professionals doing about concussions?

A: At _____, professionals are _____.

1. VA CSTE Brain Bank:

2. Mater Dei High School:

💬 Summarize

Explain how concussions affect athletes. Include the key idea and important details.

📝 Stretch Text

Turn to page 194 to read a magazine article about the effects of concussions.

Using Approximation

Put your tablet on the ta/ble.

Sometimes, you need to try different strategies and pronunciations to read new words.

Sound out a word with the stress on different syllables or break the syllables in different places until the word sounds right.

Mark It

Draw a line between the syllables. (Circle) the stressed syllable. Pronounce the word, using approximation.

1. magic

2. before

3. flavor

4. subtract

5. puzzle

6. surprise

Split It

Break the words into syllables. Use approximation to read the words. (Circle) the syllables with schwa sounds.

1. random _____ _____

2. agree _____ _____

3. happen _____ _____

4. circus _____ _____

5. avoid _____ _____

6. excellent _____ _____ _____

Sort It

Write each word from the word list in the correct box. The first one is done for you.

drastic	lilac	label	final	cotton	solo
dental	photo	infant	connect	control	allow

Short Vowel First Syllable	Long Vowel First Syllable	Schwa First Syllable
drastic		

Word Hunt

Fill in the missing word in each sentence. Find the word in the list.

1. The parents brought their new _____ home from the hospital.

2. Our team played in the _____ game, but we lost the tournament.

3. Don't forget to _____ your computer to a power source.

4. I took a great _____ of my cat with my new cell phone.

5. You have to learn to _____ your speed on a skateboard.

6. I had a _____ emergency when I knocked out my two front teeth.

Write an Informative Paragraph

Prompt *How do concussions harm athletes?*

📄 Prewrite

Review Text 1 on pages 146–147. ★Star details about how concussions affect athletes. Write down two examples from the text.

My Notes

Text Evidence	In My Own Words
"Concussions are brain injuries."	Hits to the head can hurt the brain.

💬 Academic Discussion

Take turns asking and answering questions with a partner.

Q: How do concussions affect athletes?

A: Concussions affect athletes by _____.

Q: How can teams protect players?

A: Teams can protect players by _____.

Read an example of a topic sentence. Then use your notes to answer the prompt.

Topic Sentence

A topic sentence states the key idea of the paragraph.

Prompt: How does sleep affect students?

Sleep can affect students' performance in school.

_____

_____

_____

_____

_____

_____

_____

_____

_____

_____

_____

 **Revise**

Read your writing and check your spelling. Make sure your paragraph starts with a topic sentence that states the key idea.

Read Primary Sources

Student athletes need a heads up on how to **prevent** and treat concussions. The Centers for Disease Control and Prevention is a government group. It created this fact sheet to educate athletes.

HEADS·UP
CONCUSSION IN HIGH SCHOOL SPORTS

A FACT SHEET FOR ATHLETES

How can I prevent a concussion?

It's different for every sport. But there are steps you can take to protect yourself from concussion.

- Follow your coach's rules for safety and the rules of the sport.
- Practice good sportsmanship at all times.
- Use the proper sports equipment, including personal protective equipment (such as helmets). In order for equipment to protect you, it must be:
  - Appropriate for the game, position, and activity
  - Well maintained
  - Properly fitted
  - Used every time you play

What should I do if I think I have a concussion?

- **Tell your coaches and your parents.** Never ignore a bump, blow, or jolt to the head. Also, tell your coach if one of your teammates might have a concussion.
- **Get a medical check up.** A health care professional can tell you if you have had a concussion and when you are OK to return to play.
- **Give yourself time to recover.** If you have had a concussion, your brain needs time to heal. While your brain is still healing, you are much more likely to have a second concussion. Second or later concussions can cause permanent brain damage, and even death in rare cases. Severe brain injury can change your whole life.

It's better to miss one game than the whole season.

February 2005

DEPARTMENT OF HEALTH AND HUMAN SERVICES
CENTERS FOR DISEASE CONTROL AND PREVENTION

Build Word Knowledge

Target Word Read and rate each Target Word.*	Meaning Complete the Target Word meanings.
prevent *pre•vent* *(verb)* [1] [2] [3] [4]	to _____ something from happening
recover *re•cov•er* *(verb)* [1] [2] [3] [4]	to get _____ after an injury or illness

* Rating Scale [1] = I don't know it at all. [3] = I think I know the word.
[2] = I've seen it or heard it. [4] = I know it and use it.

Analyze

Use the fact sheet to answer the questions.

1. What is one way athletes can prevent concussions?

   One way athletes can prevent concussions is _____

   _____

2. What should you do if you think a teammate has a concussion?

   If you think a teammate has a concussion, you should _____

   _____

3. What information appears in bold type on the fact sheet? Why?

   The fact sheet uses bold type for _____

   _____

   This information is bold because _____

   _____

Text-Based Questioning

Comprehension

1. What is a sentence that expresses the author's opinion?

_____

_____

_____

_____

_____

2. What evidence supports the author's claim that student athletes deserve more protection than pro football players?

_____

_____

_____

_____

_____

_____

Vocabulary & Language

3. What does *measures* mean in paragraph 3?

_____

_____

Word Analysis

Circle the S.M.A.R.T. words with short vowel sounds. Underline the words with long vowel sounds.

TOWN TRIBUNE **OPINION**

BY ANGELA KIRKWOOD

Protecting Our Players

When **pro** football stars take the field, they put their brains at **risk**. But at least they are adults who have weighed the risks and rewards.

What happens to players who are still in high school? The vast majority will never earn a **dime** playing football. Yet, they risk the same head injuries that plague NFL stars. And these injuries cause even worse damage to teenage brains that are still developing.

Nathan Stiles, 17, died from football-related brain injuries.

Shouldn't schools take stronger measures to protect young brains? Consider what happened to Nathan Stiles. At 17 years old, Stiles had a bright future. The high school senior from Spring Hill, Kansas, was a straight-A student. He was homecoming king and a varsity athlete.

On October 1, 2010, Stiles sustained a concussion during a football game. By late October, his family doctor cleared Nathan to play again.

On October 28, the young running back took the field. At first, Stiles seemed to be in fine form. He scored two touchdowns.

But just before halftime, Stiles walked off the field. He complained of a severe headache. Moments later, he collapsed. Then, he had a seizure.

A helicopter ambulance took Stiles to a medical center. Doctors discovered that his brain was hemorrhaging. Surgeons stopped the bleeding.

However, his brain was very swollen. It could not communicate with his heart and lungs. Those organs shut down. The next morning, Stiles died.

WORDS TO KNOW!

seizure: a sudden attack in which the body moves uncontrollably

hemorrhaging: bleeding severely

Academic Discussion

Key Idea

Q: What is the key idea of this part of the op-ed?

A: The key idea is _____.

_____

_____

_____

Important Details

Q: What happened to Nathan Stiles?

A: On _____, Stiles _____.

1. October 1, 2010:

2. October 28, 2010:

3. October 29, 2010:

Summarize

Explain what happened to Nathan Stiles. Include the key idea and important details.

📖 Text-Based Questioning

Comprehension

1. What is "second-impact syndrome"?

_____

_____

_____

_____

_____

_____

2. How does the author think schools can better protect athletes?

_____

_____

_____

_____

_____

_____

Vocabulary & Language

3. What does the phrase "aced a test" mean in paragraph 5?

_____

_____

_____

🔍 Word Analysis

(Circle) the S.M.A.R.T. words with short vowel sounds. Underline the words with long vowel sounds.

TOWN TRIBUNE **OPINION**

An autopsy revealed that Stiles died from "second-impact syndrome." This is when someone gets **hit** in the head while still recovering from an earlier concussion.

Stiles's parents donated his brain to the VA CSTE Brain Bank. Dr. Ann McKee examined it. At 17, Stiles already had CTE. Dr. McKee was shocked at what she found. "It tells you that we've really got to protect our kids," she said.

Stiles is the youngest CTE case Dr. McKee has studied. But doctors can't confirm CTE until the victim is dead. Who knows how many living students might **be** afflicted?

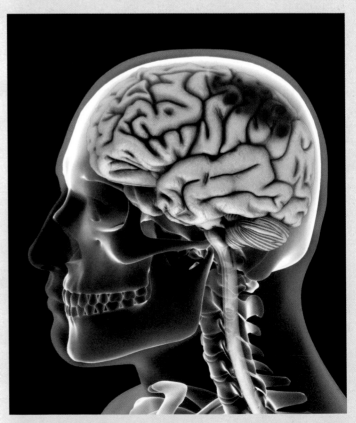

Stiles's first concussion caused a subdural hematoma. It is a collection of blood on the brain's surface.

About 60,000 **high** school football players suffer concussions each year. How should schools protect athletes? Many schools require medical exams before players with concussions return to athletics. Some also require students to **pass** tests that show their brains are working normally.

However, Stiles had his doctor's permission to play football. He aced a **math** test just days before he died. And yet, his brain had not healed from the concussion.

Schools must change the way teens play sports. All sports can teach teamwork and discipline, and even lead to college scholarships. But the risks should not outweigh these rewards.

High school football needs new rules to prevent hard hits. Also, students who get concussions should be out for the rest of the season. Or maybe they should stop playing forever. **No** student's mind—or life—is worth risking for a game.

WORDS TO KNOW!

autopsy: an exam of a corpse to find the cause of death

afflicted: suffering

Word Count 467   **Lexile** 720L

Academic Discussion

Key Idea

Q: What is the key idea of this part of the op-ed?

A: The key idea is _____.

_____
_____

Important Details

Q: How should schools protect athletes?

A: _____ way schools should protect athletes is _____.

1. One:

2. Another:

3. A third:

Summarize

Explain the author's argument. Include the key idea and important details.

Stretch Text

Turn to page 194 to read fiction about an injured athlete.

Using Patterns to Determine Vowel Sounds

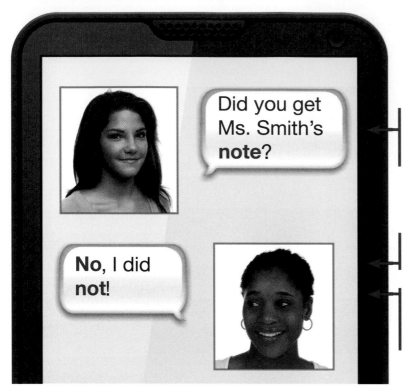

The pattern of consonants and vowels in a word can determine the sound of the vowels.

When a vowel is followed by a consonant and a final e, it is usually long. (**VCe**)

If a syllable ends with a vowel, the vowel sound is usually long. (**CV**)

If a syllable ends with a consonant, the vowel sound is usually short. (**CVC**)

Mark It

Circle the words with short vowel sounds. Underline the words with long vowel sounds. Pronounce the word pairs.

1. be   bet

2. wet   we

3. so   son

4. no   nod

5. his   hi

6. shed   she

Split It

Divide each word into syllables. Circle the syllable with a VCe pattern.

1. alone

2. athlete

3. describe

4. inside

5. donate

6. refuse

Sort It

Read the words from left to right. Sort them by pattern and vowel sound.

so	mope	not	we	hike	hip
wet	note	rub	hi	fast	grade

CV Long Vowel Sound	CVC Short Vowel Sound	VCe Long Vowel Sound

Sentence Solver

Choose the correct word to fill each blank.

1. You will help get _____ of pollution if you _____ a bike.   **rid   ride**

2. Our _____ is to take a _____ to Florida for vacation.   **plan   plane**

3. I was feeling _____ until I saw a _____ in the water.   **fin   fine**

4. I hurt my _____ when I did the dance _____   **spin   spine**

5. My _____ Armando turned _____ when he saw the snake.   **pal   pale**

6. Our older brother let _____ _____ his surfboard.   **us   use**

Write an Argument

Prompt *How should schools protect athletes from head injuries?*

Prewrite

Review Text 3 on pages 154–157. ★Star dangers that athletes face from head injuries. Write down three examples from the text.

My Notes

Text Evidence	In My Own Words
"And these injuries cause even worse damage to teenage brains that are still developing."	Concussions hurt teenagers more because their brains aren't fully formed.

Academic Discussion

Take turns asking and answering questions with a partner.

Q: Why are teens at greater risk from head injuries than adults?

A: Teens are at greater risk because _____.

Q: How did a concussion lead to Nathan Stiles's death?

A: A concussion led to Nathan Stiles's death because _____.

Read an example of a detail sentence. Then use your notes to answer the prompt.

Detail Sentences

Detail sentences support the topic sentence. They provide evidence such as facts and examples.

Adolescents need about nine hours of sleep per night to function at their best.

_____

_____

_____

_____

_____

_____

_____

_____

_____

_____

_____

 **Revise**

Read your writing and check your spelling. Make sure your detail sentences support the topic sentence and provide evidence.

Hold a Class Debate

Should teenagers play contact sports? Choose a position and argue it. Use text evidence to support your position.

EVALUATE EVIDENCE Look back at the texts. Write about two ways that concussions can affect teenagers.

A. _____

_____

B. _____

_____

BRAINSTORM List the pros and cons of contact sports.

Pros	Cons

STATE YOUR POSITION Which side of the debate are you on?

Teenagers should/should not (circle one) play contact sports because

_____

_____

TAKE NOTES Prepare for the debate. As each side argues its claims, record key ideas.

DEBATE: *Should teenagers play contact sports?*

OPENING STATEMENT: *Teenagers should* _____

_____

_____

_____

OUR SIDE'S POSITION:	**POSSIBLE RESPONSE:**
A. _____	A. _____
B. _____	B. _____

SUMMARY/CLOSING STATEMENT:

In conclusion, contact sports are

_____

_____

_____

_____

✓ Self Check

Put a check mark in the box if you can answer "yes" to the following questions.

❏ Did you include evidence from the texts that supports your position?

❏ Did you address the other side's arguments?

Refugee Life: Starting Over

What challenges do refugees face?

All over the world, millions of people have had to leave their homes. They are called refugees. They have to find new places to live because their old homes are not safe anymore.

TEXT 1 News Article

Promoting Peace

Lucy Kayee faced many challenges as a refugee. Now she works for peace.

TEXT 2 Map

Read Primary Sources

A map shows the features of part of the largest refugee camp in the world.

TEXT 3 Magazine Article

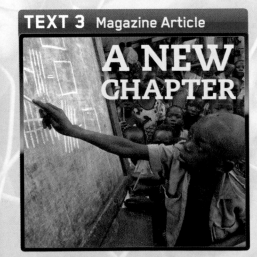

A NEW CHAPTER

Classes in refugee camps can be crowded. Some are even held outside.

Anchor Understanding

Watch the video and complete the outline.

I. Like many other people in their country, the Diyali family had to leave Bhutan because of their language and ___customs.___

II. In the refugee camp, the huts they lived in were uncomfortable, the teachers were abusive, and the water _____ was dangerous.

III. Fortunately, an _____ that helps refugees move into permanent homes rescued the Diyalis.

IV. Now Bala Diyali is studying _____ in college.

V. The Diyalis are happy in America, but they still eat _____ foods and celebrate the festivals from home.

Discuss & Write

Take turns asking and answering questions.

Q: What are some of the challenges of living in a refugee camp?

A: Some of the challenges of living in a refugee camp are _____

_____

_____

_____

Q: Why was moving to America challenging for the Diyalis?

A: Moving to America was challenging for the Diyalis because _____

_____

_____

_____

Build Word Knowledge

Target Word	Meaning	Examples
Read and rate each Target Word.*	**Complete the Target Word meanings.**	**Finish the Target Word examples below.**

international
in•ter•na•tion•al
(adjective)
p. 169

`1` `2` `3` `4`

involving more

than one

_____

- I go to an **international** school

  that has students from _____

  _____

  _____

- To go to _____

  _____, I need

  to buy an **international** flight.

protect
pro•tect
(verb)
p. 168

`1` `2` `3` `4`

to keep

_____

- _____

  wear special clothing to **protect**

  themselves from injuries.

- People who ride motorcycles

  wear _____

  to **protect** their bodies.

refugee
ref•u•gee
(noun)
p. 168

`1` `2` `3` `4`

a person who

leaves home to

escape harm or

_____

- The **refugee** left _____

  _____

- The **refugee** returned when the

  _____ was over.

* Rating Scale

`1` = I don't know it at all. `3` = I think I know the word.
`2` = I've seen it or heard it. `4` = I know it and use it.

166 MODULE 8

Word Families

Complete the meaning and examples for the Target Words.

Target Word	Meaning	Examples
nation *na•tion* *(noun)* p. 168	a _____ or the group of people who live there	• A **nation** I would like to visit is _____ • People in a **nation** usually share _____ _____

international

Target Word	Meaning	Examples
national *na•tion•al* *(adjective)* p. 179	related to a _____ as a whole	• A **national** symbol of the United States is _____ _____ • **National** teams compete in _____ _____

Text-Based Questioning

Comprehension

1. Why did Lucy Kayee and her stepfather move to the United States?

_____

_____

_____

_____

2. What problem does Lucy's community in the United States face?

_____

_____

_____

_____

_____

Vocabulary & Language

3. What does the word *fled* mean in paragraph 2?

_____

_____

4. Could the author use *left* instead?

_____

_____

_____

Word Analysis

Circle the S.M.A.R.T. words that are homophones. Underline the words that are homographs.

Promoting Peace

By SHAKIMA PEARSON

Lucy Kayee is a **refugee** from Liberia, a **nation** in West Africa. Her country was at war for many years. She hasn't seen her brother since he was kidnapped and forced to become a child soldier.

When Lucy was five, her family fled to a refugee camp. Beatings were frequent, and one girl killed herself after her hair was torn out. Lucy's family members had no one to **protect** them from violence. **Their lives** were **still** in danger.

In 2002, when Lucy was six years old, she moved to Minneapolis, Minnesota, with her stepfather. At first, Lucy's new life was dangerous, too. Her stepfather abused her, and a friend was killed in a shooting.

Lucy Kayee shares her experiences at a Youth Empowerment Program event.

"It's sad [because] I came **here** to get away from violence," Lucy said.

In 2006, Lucy went into foster care. She was a troubled child. By age twelve, she was about five years behind in school. However, Lucy decided to catch up. "I **just** wanted to prove [my stepfather] wrong so bad that I just studied so much," she said.

Lucy's foster mother sent her to counseling for her anger. The counselor introduced Lucy to a program that empowers teens to be community leaders.

Today, Lucy works to bring **peace** to her community. She plans to become an immigration lawyer whose **international** work will help other refugees.

Lucy and other teen leaders discuss their ideas about stopping violence.

WORDS TO KNOW!

foster care: a program in which people care for children who have been removed from their parents

Word Count 221   Lexile 740L

Academic Discussion

Key Idea

Q: What is the key idea of the article?

A: The key idea of the article is _____.

_____

_____

Important Details

Q: What was Lucy's life like in each place?

A: In _____, Lucy _____.

1. Liberia:

2. The United States (at first):

3. The United States (now):

Summarize

Explain Lucy Kayee's experiences as a refugee. Include the key idea and important details.

Stretch Text

Turn to page 195 to read a news article about refugees in Somalia.

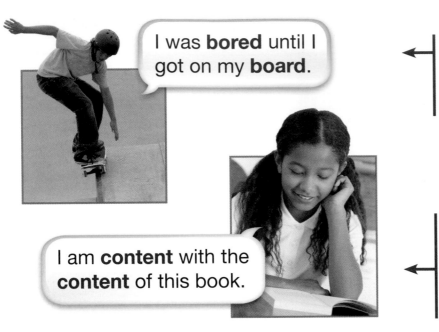

Recognizing Homophones and Homographs

I was **bored** until I got on my **board**.

Homophones have the same pronunciation, but different spellings and meanings.

I am **content** with the **content** of this book.

Homographs have the same spelling, but different meanings. Homographs are sometimes pronounced differently, too.

Match Homophones

Draw a line between each pair of homophones.

1. wait	**a.** deer
2. bear	**b.** pour
3. dear	**c.** weight
4. male	**d.** see
5. poor	**e.** bare
6. sea	**f.** mail

Determine Meanings

Circle the correct homophone for each meaning.

1. opposite of female:	mail	male
2. a body of water:	sea	see
3. a large animal:	bear	bare
4. having little money:	pour	poor
5. measured in pounds:	weight	wait
6. an animal with antlers:	deer	dear

Context Clues

Write the correct homophones to complete the sentences.

1. That store can _____ you a new _____ phone. (cell, sell)

2. I will _____ him a gift at the shop _____ the park. (buy, by)

3. The baby _____ where his lips and _____ are. (knows, nose)

4. The _____ must have _____ when the doctor's office is busy.

   (patience, patients)

5. Have you _____ that movie _____ (scene, seen)

6. How much is bus _____ to get to the _____ (fair, fare)

7. _____ you know when our science paper about rain and

   _____ is _____ (dew, do, due)

8. _____ going to stop at the animal hospital because _____

   dog is _____ (their, there, they're)

Match Homographs

Write each homograph next to the pair of clues it matches and pronounce it.

> content   dove   batter   fair

1. what cake is made from: _____

   the hitter in a baseball game: _____

2. the past tense of dive: _____

   a kind of bird: _____

3. pretty or pleasant: _____

   a festival or carnival: _____

4. the information in a book: _____

   happy or satisfied: _____

Write an Informative Paragraph

Prompt | *How did Lucy Kayee respond to challenges she faced?*

📃 Prewrite

Reread Text 1 on pages 168–169. ★Star at least two challenges Lucy Kayee faced. Write down two examples from the text.

My Notes

Text Evidence	In My Own Words
"Her country was at war for many years."	Soldiers were fighting in Liberia.

💬 Academic Discussion

Take turns asking and answering questions with a partner.

Q: What is a challenge Lucy Kayee faced?

A: One challenge Lucy faced was _____.

Q: How did Lucy respond?

A: Lucy responded by _____.

Write

Read an example of transition words. Then use your notes to answer the prompt.

Transition Words

Transition words and phrases introduce and connect ideas in a paragraph. Here are some examples:

first	therefore	according to the text
also	however	lastly
for example	another	in conclusion

In addition, Lucy struggled in school and fell about
<u>(transition)</u>

five years behind.

_____

_____

_____

_____

_____

_____

_____

_____

_____

_____

_____

 **Revise**

Read your writing and check your spelling. Make sure your paragraph includes transition words that introduce and connect ideas.

Read Primary Sources

Dagahaley is one of three refugee camps in Dadaab, Kenya. Many refugees fled civil war in Somalia. Others arrived after dry conditions left them without food. A camp worker might use this map to find the health posts, schools, and the market.

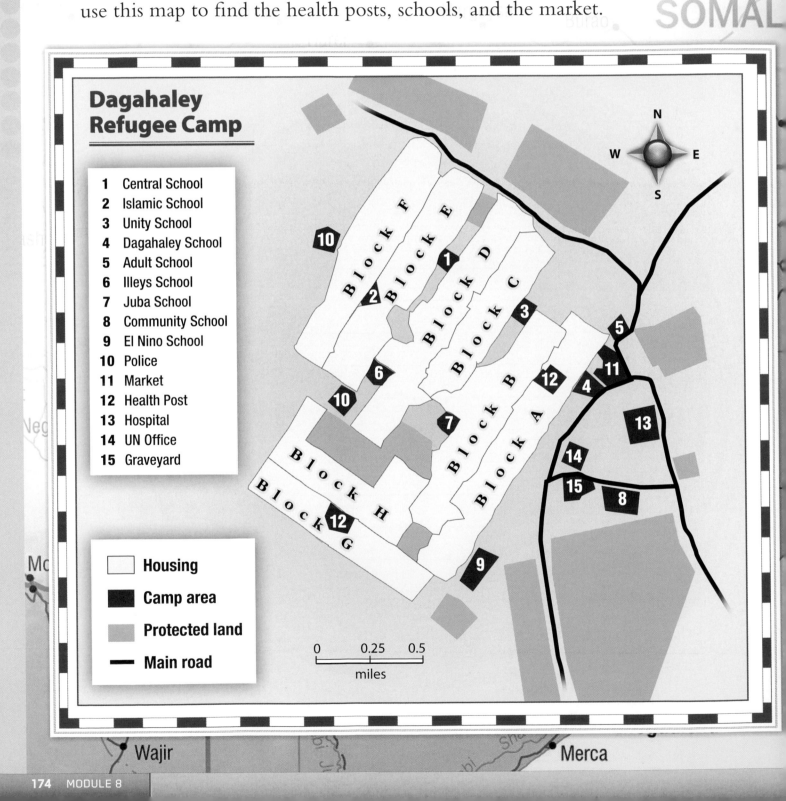

Dagahaley Refugee Camp

1 Central School
2 Islamic School
3 Unity School
4 Dagahaley School
5 Adult School
6 Illeys School
7 Juba School
8 Community School
9 El Nino School
10 Police
11 Market
12 Health Post
13 Hospital
14 UN Office
15 Graveyard

Housing
Camp area
Protected land
Main road

0   0.25   0.5
miles

Build Word Knowledge

Target Word Read and rate each Target Word.*	Meaning Complete the Target Word meanings.
legend leg•end (noun) 1 2 3 4	a list that explains the _____ and _____ used on a map
scale scale (noun) 1 2 3 4	the relationship between the _____ of a map and the actual size of the place it represents

* Rating Scale
1 = I don't know it at all.
2 = I've seen it or heard it.
3 = I think I know the word.
4 = I know it and use it.

Analyze

Use the map to answer the questions.

1. What color are the buildings on the map where workers help refugees?

   The buildings where workers help refugees are _____ because they are

   _____

2. How far is it from the Adult School to the hospital?

   A: 0.1 miles   **C:** 0.5 miles

   B: 0.25 miles   **D:** 1 mile

3. What camp areas are most important for refugees? Why?

   A camp area that is important for refugees is _____

   because _____

   _____

   _____

Text-Based Questioning

Comprehension

1. What does the author mean when she says "education can help [refugees] start over"?

_____

_____

_____

_____

_____

2. Does the author think schools in Dadaab, Kenya, need improvement? Use text evidence to support your response.

_____

_____

_____

_____

_____

_____

Vocabulary & Language

3. What is a synonym for the word *additional* in paragraph 5?

_____

_____

Word Analysis

Underline the base word in each S.M.A.R.T. word that is part of a word family.

A NEW CHAPTER

Refugee students learn at camps around the world and at schools in the United States.

by Jessica Warren

Imagine your class had 100 students. That is a reality for some of the millions of children who are refugees. Education can help refugee children start over. **Unfortunately,** only about 40 percent go to school.

The Largest Refugee Camp

Dadaab is a town in the East African nation of Kenya. Dadaab is home to three refugee camps. Together, these camps make up the world's largest refugee complex.

Dadaab refugee camps house more than 400,000 refugees, **mostly** from Somalia. About 221,000 Dadaab refugees are children of school age.

Like most schools in refugee camps, Dadaab's 36 schools face many challenges. They are **overcrowded** and lack adequate funding and supplies.

Classes in refugee camps can be crowded.

On the first day of school in 2011, only one in three children in Dadaab went to school. Some have just arrived at the camps. The camps need an **additional** 75 schools and more teachers, too. On average, each teacher has about 100 students. Often, the teachers are refugees themselves.

Hungry for Knowledge and Lunch

At a refugee school in Luthaya, South Sudan, children attend classes outdoors and sit on piles of bricks instead of chairs. The school does not have money to provide lunches, and some students don't eat breakfast before school. Therefore, many students go hungry during the school day.

"They want to learn, but the problem is hunger," principal Alphonse Moi said. "They can't learn when they are hungry."

WORDS TO KNOW!

complex: a group of buildings

adequate: enough

Academic Discussion

Key Idea

Q: What is the key idea of this part of the article?

A: The key idea is _____.

_____

_____

Important Details

Q: What challenges did refugee students face in each country?

A: A challenge refugee students faced in _____ was _____.

1. Kenya:

2. South Sudan:

Summarize

Explain what schools are like at refugee camps. Include the key idea and important details.

📖 Text-Based Questioning

Comprehension

1. What is one way Mooreland Heights helped refugee students?

_____

_____

_____

_____

_____

2. Why does the author describe the summer institute in Phoenix?

_____

_____

_____

_____

_____

Vocabulary & Language

3. What does the word *interpreter* mean in paragraph 4?

_____

_____

_____

_____

_____

🔍 Word Analysis

<u>Underline</u> the base word in each S.M.A.R.T. word that is part of a word family.

Learning in America

More than 800,000 young refugees are living in the United States. Some schools have set up special classes for refugees. Some communities have even established special schools just for international students.

Columbus Global Academy, in Columbus, Ohio, is one such school. About half of its 460 international students are refugees.

Every class has an **assistant** who translates for students. Many refugee students had never gone to school in their home countries, and some of them don't know how to write. At Columbus Global Academy, these students learn school routines.

A teacher at Mooreland Heights Elementary works with refugee students.

Supporting Refugees

Mooreland Heights Elementary School in Tennessee set up a special class for five refugees from Burundi, in Africa. An interpreter helped translate English into their **national** language, Kirundi.

A play therapist also helped the students deal with the effects of trauma they experienced in war-torn Burundi. Refugees often suffer from emotional problems, such as post-traumatic stress **disorder**. This disorder can result when someone survives serious danger, and its symptoms include nightmares, fear, and **difficulty** concentrating.

In Arizona, Phoenix Union High School District has more than 500 refugee students. The district has a special summer institute for refugees. The students learn English, make friends, and adjust to life in America. For example, students go bowling and visit local grocery stores.

Omar Fidow is a teenage refugee from Somalia. "This program is good for us," he said. "We're learning how the city is. I'm figuring out what I need to know."

WORDS TO KNOW!

translates: changes words into another language

routines: usual orders or ways of doing things

Word Count **473**   Lexile **810L**

Academic Discussion

Key Idea

Q: What is the key idea of this part of the article?

A: The key idea is _____.

_____

_____

Important Details

Q: How did each school or district help refugee students?

A: _____ helped refugee students by _____.

1. Columbus Global Academy:

2. Mooreland Heights Elementary:

3. Phoenix Union High School District:

Summarize

Explain how schools in the United States help refugees. Include the key idea and important details.

Stretch Text

Turn to page 195 to read fiction about a young newcomer.

Recognizing Word Families

> I'm going down to the basement to look for some base words.

> I think you already found the **base** word in **basement**!

A **base word** is a word to which other word parts, like prefixes, suffixes, and endings, may be added.

A **base word family** is the group of words that share the same base word.

Sometimes you can figure out the meaning of a word if you think about another word from the same family.

Mark It

Underline the base words. (Circle) the prefixes, suffixes, and endings.

1. helpful

2. reread

3. slowly

4. unwanted

5. preschool

6. uncommonness

Write It

Underline the base word. (Circle) the prefix or suffix. Write the word's meaning.

1. preview _____

2. replay _____

3. saddest _____

4. skillful _____

5. misbehave _____

6. unkind _____

Sort It

Underline the base words in the word list. Then, write the base words at the top of the chart. Sort the words by base word family.

unkind	unevenness	kindly	kindness
friendly	unfriendly	uneven	evenly
unkindly	unfriendliness	friendliness	evenness

kind	_____	_____

Sentence Solver

Choose the correct word from the word list to fill in each blank.

1. It was difficult to ride our bikes because of the _____ of the road.

2. The dog's owner said it was safe to pet it because it was a _____ animal.

3. The basketball game was exciting because the teams were

_____ matched.

4. Helping an older person carry heavy bags is an act of _____

5. Tom was elected president of the class because of his _____ to everyone.

Write an Argument

Prompt | *How should schools help refugees?*

Prewrite

Review Text 3 on pages 176–179. ★Star details that describe how school can be difficult for refugee students. Write down two examples from the text.

My Notes

Text Evidence	In My Own Words
"On average, each teacher has about 100 students."	Crowded classes can have 100 students.

Academic Discussion

Take turns asking and answering questions with a partner. Listen and take notes.

Q: How can school be difficult for refugees?

A: School can be difficult for refugees because _____.

Q: How have schools helped refugees?

A: To help refugees, schools _____.

 **Write**

Read an example of a concluding sentence. Then use your notes to answer the prompt.

Concluding Sentence

A concluding sentence sums up the paragraph or explains why the topic is important. In an argument, it may offer a recommendation.

Prompt: How can schools help students get enough sleep?

Therefore, high schools should start later to ensure students can perform at their best.

_____

_____

_____

_____

_____

_____

_____

_____

_____

_____

Revise

Read your writing and check your spelling. Make sure your paragraph ends with a concluding sentence that sums up the paragraph or offers a recommendation.

Create a Welcome Brochure

A group of refugees have become students at your school. Write a brochure to help new students learn about your school.

GATHER INFORMATION Look back at the texts. Write two problems that many refugee students face.

A. _____

_____

B. _____

_____

SOLVE PROBLEMS For each problem you listed, describe the programs at your school that can help.

Program	Contact People	Location

CREATE YOUR BROCHURE In each section below, describe the features of your school that will help refugees. Give each section a title.

WELCOME TO YOUR NEW SCHOOL!

Section 1: _____

_____

_____

_____

_____

_____

_____

Section 2: _____

_____

_____

_____

_____

_____

_____

PRESENT YOUR BROCHURE Share your brochure with the group. Use gestures to emphasize important points.

✓ Self Check

Put a check mark in the box if you can answer "yes" to the following questions.

❑ Does each section have a title that says what it is about?

❑ Did you include information that would help refugees?

SYSTEM 44 ®

*NEXT*GENERATION

Stretch Texts & Fluency Practice

Moderate 1 | 1210L

STRETCH TEXT 1 Nonfiction

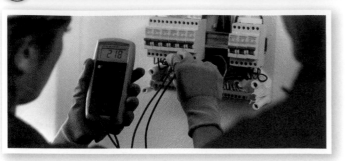

from

The 6 Most Important Decisions You'll Ever Make

BY SEAN COVEY

Does going to college really pay off? Absolutely!

Computer support specialists with no high school diploma earn just over $31,000 per year, which is among the better-paying jobs for someone with that level of education. However, workers with a high school diploma or a two-year degree earn salaries in the low-to-mid-$50,000 range. Computer support specialists with a four-year degree earn $74,000, while those with a master's degree earn $92,000. Some difference!

An electrician without a high school education has a median salary of about $32,000, which is a really high-paying job for a high school dropout. On the other hand, with more education, you could become an electrical and electronics engineer, and earn $57,000 with a two-year degree, $66,000 with a four-year degree, $76,000 with a master's degree, and $112,000 with a doctoral degree. Now, if that doesn't motivate you to stick with school, what will?

WORDS TO KNOW!

median: the middle number in a set of numbers listed in order

doctoral degree: the highest level of a degree

Moderate 1 | NP

STRETCH TEXT 2 Poetry

from

This Full House

BY VIRGINIA EUWER WOLFF

Jolly holds the certificate in one hand and
   shakes hands
and keeps looking at the G.E.D. she
   has just earned.
She goes to the microphone,
moves it from where it was
for the very tall person before her
down to her mouth level
and she starts:
"I thought I never get here.
Um.
I thought I *would* never get here.
It was hard."

"I do not thank those
that did not give me a chance to make it.
They betted against me
but I won. Here I am."

Jolly, who has for so long lived sideways,
walks straight and upright to her chair
and holds her G.E.D.
certificate in front of
her like a map.
Everyone claps
till the waves of her
gown stop jiggling.

WORDS TO KNOW!

G.E.D.: General Educational Degree; an alternative to a high school diploma

earned: worked to achieve a result

STRETCH TEXT 1 Memoir

Moderate 1 · 1010L

from

The Red Circle

BY BRANDON WEBB

Our day started at 5:00 a.m. on the beach with grueling PT and from there on was a never-ending endurance contest of both flesh and will. By the second week my hands were shredded. I developed two calluses on my left hand and three on my right, all five of them soon ripped off with a half-inch of flesh exposed from doing those wet and sandy push-ups on the beach. When the class corpsman applied tincture benzoate to seal the wounds and prevent infection, it felt like he was sticking a hot iron into each wound. I could barely stand up in the morning. My arms were aching. My body was in complete breakdown.

WORDS TO KNOW!

grueling: very difficult
PT: Physical Training

STRETCH TEXT 2 News Article

Moderate 1 · 870L

from

The Guys Who Got bin Laden

Scholastic Scope, September 5, 2011
BY KRISTIN LEWIS

The SEALs chosen for the bin Laden mission spent months preparing; meticulous planning is a hallmark of the Navy SEALs. They planned for any possibility, including a downed helicopter. So when the chopper crashed, they knew exactly what to do.

Without hesitation, they climbed out of the helicopter's wreckage, sprinted toward the wall of the compound, and placed explosives on the door. In a matter of minutes, the SEALs stormed the compound, located bin Laden, and executed him. Next they seized documents, computers, and other materials. These items contained the names of other Al Qaeda members and plans for another attack on the U.S. This information could save thousands of lives.

Then the SEALs boarded another helicopter and vanished into the night.

WORDS TO KNOW!

meticulous: very careful and precise
seized: quickly took something

STRETCH TEXT 1 Nonfiction   Moderate 1   1160L

from

Extra Lives: Why Video Games Matter

BY TOM BISSELL

[Art Director Henry] LaBounta immediately admitted that "realistic humans" are "one of the most difficult things" for game designers to create. "A real challenge," he said, "is hair." Aside from convincing coifs, two things video-game characters generally need are what he called "model fidelity" (do they resemble real people?) and "motion fidelity" (do they move like real people?). Neither, he said, necessarily corresponded to straight realism.

One thing that routinely frustrated him, LaBounta said, was when a video-game character walks into a wall and persists, stupidly, in walking. Allowing the character to react to the wall would be the result of a "recognition mechanic," whereby the character is able to sense his surroundings with no input from the player. Of course, this would not be intelligence but *awareness*.

WORDS TO KNOW!

fidelity: faithfulness
corresponded: related
recognition: the act of knowing or seeing something

STRETCH TEXT 2 News Article   Moderate 2   1240L

from

Striiv: Fitness Meets Gaming, Minus the Console

***The Los Angeles Times**, October 26, 2011*
BY ALEX PHAM

Parts of the games business may be in need of life support, but some genres such as fitness games are powering on despite a swoon in consumer spending.

The latest entrant in this field is Striiv (pronounced "*strive*"), a gadget the size of a Smalltoids tin that tracks the number of steps or stairs its owner makes.

Users can also donate their steps to various causes, via GlobalGiving, an organization that disperses donations to about 1,000 grassroots projects. Take 18,000 steps, and Striiv will donate enough money to provide a day's worth of clean drinking water for a child in South Africa. Alternatively, users can protect Tanzania's rain forest or fund polio vaccinations.

"Nothing's new about it," [gaming expert Wanda] Meloni said. "But it's so intuitive and easy that it can be very appealing to the mass market."

WORDS TO KNOW!

console: a full-size video game system
genres: categories
entrant: someone or something that takes part in a contest

Moderate 2 | 840L

L STRETCH TEXT 1 Fiction

from
The Hunger Games
BY SUZANNE COLLINS

"People are intrigued but no one knows who you are. The impression you make tomorrow will decide exactly what I can get you in terms of sponsors," says Haymitch.

Having watched the tribute interviews all my life, I know there's truth to what he's saying. If you appeal to the crowd, either by being humorous or brutal or eccentric, you gain favor.

"What's Peeta's approach? Or am I not allowed to ask?" I say.

"Likeable. He has a sort of self-deprecating humor naturally," says Haymitch. "Whereas when you open your mouth, you come across more as sullen and hostile."

WORDS TO KNOW!

sponsors: people who pay for something in return for publicity
sullen: angry and silent

Moderate 2 | 990L

i STRETCH TEXT 2 News Article

from
Why Videos Go Viral
CBSNews.com, February 28, 2012
BY BAILEY JOHNSON

Forty-eight hours of video are uploaded on YouTube every minute. It seems like an impossible number, and it is evidence of just how much content goes online every day. With all those hours and hours of video, how does anything ever become "viral"?

The main points of what make Internet videos popular are not new. Novelty, unexpectedness, humor. These things have always been popular, but the ability to participate in a viral video—either through sharing with friends, commenting on posts, or even making tribute videos—is what defines the medium. We didn't just dislike Rebecca Black's "Friday" video, we disliked it so much we had to share it. That's the sure sign of a hit.

WORDS TO KNOW!

novelty: the quality of being new and unusual

STRETCH TEXT 1 Fiction

Moderate 2 | 810L

from
The Langoliers
BY STEPHEN KING

Brian began to hear it before he was halfway across the waiting room and by the time he had joined the others, it was impossible to believe it was an auditory hallucination.

He could feel the hairs on the nape of his neck stiffening in response to that sound. He looked at the others and saw identical expressions of frightened dismay on every face. Nick was controlling himself the best, and Bethany looked the most deeply scared, but they all heard the same thing in the sound.

Bad.

Something bad on the way. *Hurrying.*

"We *do* have to get out of here!" Bethany said. Her voice was loud and wavery. Albert put an arm around her waist and she gripped his hand in both of hers. Gripped it with panicky tightness. "We have to get out of here *right now!*"

WORDS TO KNOW!

auditory: relating to the sense of hearing
dismay: worry

STRETCH TEXT 2 Science Article

Complex 1 | 1010L

from
Hollywood, Halloween, and Horror Movies— a Killer Formula
Psychology Today, October 29, 2011
BY STUART FISCHOFF

On a general level, movie monsters, horror movies, and spine tingling thrillers provide food for our imagination's nourishment. We consciously, deliberately put away the rich fears of childhood as we acquire knowledge, and temper irrational fears with rational self-talk. We also fulfill the adultified expectations of our adult peers. In so doing, we relinquish many of our superstitions with more science-based explanations. There is a cost, however: Our world of imagination is diminished, tamed into blandness. Life in Technicolor slowly fades to Black and White.

Speaking analytically for the moment, childhood fears of monsters and the supernatural are never truly banished from our adult minds; they linger like archetypes in our subconscious. Horror movies and movie monsters allow us to revisit those fears from a safe remove.

WORDS TO KNOW!

nourishment: something that feeds us
consciously: in an aware way

STRETCH TEXT 1 Short Story

Moderate 2 | 840L

from
Small Colored World
BY TERRIS MCMAHAN GRIMES

Annie Mae Williams ran a board and care facility for developmentally disabled adults out of her South Land Park home. She was a big, affable woman, in a spectacularly bad wig. It was impossible to tell her age; she could have been a hard-lived fifty, or a genetically blessed ninety.

"Some folks said he did, other folks swore he didn't. Venable the only one said she saw what happened. I'm telling you, people fell out over it, divided the whole town. You go down to Pit Pat and people still arguing about it to this very day."

"Which side were you on?"

"I stayed clear of all that mess, minded my own business, got my diploma, and left on the first thing smoking. But I tell you one thing, the wrong man went to prison."

> **WORDS TO KNOW!**
>
> **board:** meals included with housing
> **affable:** friendly and likeable

STRETCH TEXT 2 Guidebook

Moderate 2 | 1050L

from
The Right to Freedom From Searches
BY FRED RAMEN

The Fourth, Fifth, Sixth, and Eighth Amendments to the U.S. Constitution all deal with what are known as the "rights of the accused."

The Fourth Amendment concerns searches and seizures and warrants. Legally, searches and seizures refers to the ability of the government to search a person or his or her home or office and to seize items that are evidence of a crime that the person may have committed; this evidence then can be used against him or her at trial. The Fourth Amendment requires that searches and seizures must be reasonable.

A warrant is a document, usually issued by a judge, that allows the police to search a place or put a person under arrest.

> **WORDS TO KNOW!**
>
> **accused:** people said to have done something wrong
> **reasonable:** fair

Complex 1 — 1070L

STRETCH TEXT 1 Magazine Article

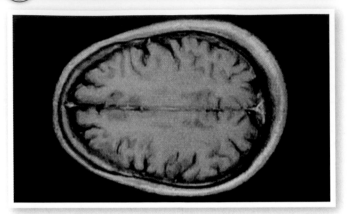

from
The Invisible Injury
Scholastic Choices, **April/May 2009**
BY SEAN MCCOLLUM

Most concussions do not cause structural damage to the brain. A concussed brain is likely to appear healthy on X-rays, CAT scans, and MRI (magnetic resonance imaging) tests. "Even if the injury is life-threatening, the tests may very well be normal," [Dr. Michael] Collins says.

The real danger has to do with the brain's neurochemistry. A hard hit to the head may trigger a chemical chain reaction. One of the effects of this reaction is a jump in the amount of energy the brain requires, according to Collins. At the same time, the brain's ability to create that energy is cut off, and there is also a sudden drop in the brain's blood flow. The result is a disruption of normal brain function that can lead to disorientation, memory loss, unconsciousness, and even death.

WORDS TO KNOW!

disruption: an interruption
disorientation: confusion, particularly about location

Complex 1 — 920L

STRETCH TEXT 2 Fiction

from
Roughnecks
BY THOMAS COCHRAN

The whole time I was in the hospital I'd hoped that somehow my injury wouldn't transfer into the real world intact. I knew that it wasn't going to go away entirely but I honestly thought that it might be less severe on the outside.

The idea that I'd be able to talk Crews into letting me into a game for one play was in the back of my mind.

At that point, football was the reason I got up in the morning. It was worth whatever I had to give to be able to play it including, I thought, the risk of permanent injury. I didn't realize that if I had been allowed to play and had seriously injured myself, I would have forfeited playing ball in the future.

WORDS TO KNOW!

intact: not broken; the same
forfeited: given up or had taken away

STRETCH TEXT 1 News Article

Complex 1 | 1070L

from

Somalia: Famine's Youngest Victims

Junior Scholastic, December 12, 2011
BY CASSANDRA NELSON

Somalia is one of the world's most dangerous countries. When its government collapsed in 1991, feuding warlords and militants overran the streets. After two decades of anarchy and civil war, much of Somalia's infrastructure has been destroyed. With no education or work, many people, kids included, have turned to violent crime or joined militant groups.

This turmoil has displaced 1.5 million people—15 percent of Somalia's population—within the country. Another million Somalis have fled to neighboring countries, including Kenya and Ethiopia.

Most of Somalia's displaced people, like Firduz and her family, end up in refugee camps. In Mogadishu, more than half the population lives in makeshift shelters. Families are crammed into tents and lack access to clean water or sanitation facilities. Improper waste disposal is causing food and water contamination and spreading disease.

> **WORDS TO KNOW!**
>
> **anarchy:** no order or control
> **infrastructure:** the basic systems of a country, such as highways and schools
> **turmoil:** a state of great confusion

STRETCH TEXT 2 Fiction

Complex 1 | 820L

from

Quiet As They Come

BY ANGIE CHAU

My name is Elle.

No one at school knows it's my fake name. My parents changed it so that I would fit better. Sometimes I wonder if they'll change my last name too. And if they do, what will become of the old me? The Vietnamese name with the two letters that match like your favorite pair of socks.

Everyone else got famous people names like Sophia Loren and Marcel, short for Marcello Mastroianni. The three boys are named after the Rat Pack, Uncle Lam's favorite group. When I ask my mom why I didn't get a cool famous name, she looks around to make sure nobody else is around and whispers, "I would never do that to you. It's like announcing you still have salt behind your ears."

If my parents want to change my last name, I will say, *please*, if I'm good can I choose this time?

> **WORDS TO KNOW!**
>
> **announcing:** saying publicly

| Series 1 | **Bats Do That?** |

Baby bats are everywhere! Bat moms can find them. 9
They use sound signals. They use smell signals. Their 18
communication is amazing! The baby bats eat. The baby 27
bats get big! 30

| Series 2 | **Art for Kicks** |

Steven is an artist. He picks a shoe. He dips his brush. 12
He dabs on a design! 17

Kids pick shoes. They pick their favorite kicks. They 26
pick kicks that fit. 30

Are you creative? Can you paint kicks? 37

| Series 3 | **Run, Jesse, Run** |

Jesse Owens ran track for the USA. In 1936, he went 11
to Germany to run in the Olympics. The German 20
dictator Hitler said Jesse could not win. But Jesse was 30
quick. His team could count on him. 37

Jesse wanted to win. And he did. He got four gold 48
medals. He demonstrated that he was the fastest 56
man alive. 58

Series 4 — Passing the Sniff Test

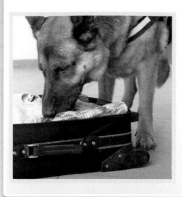

Some dogs have a special skill. They can smell trouble! 10
They do sniff tests. They can detect bombs and guns. 20
Dogs take big risks to help people. Good job, dogs! 30

Series 5 — Brain Freeze

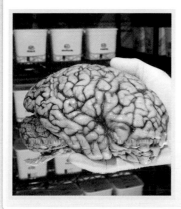

What is a brain bank? People drop off brains. 9
Scientists use them for research. 14

Luis is a brain scientist. He grabs a brain. He splits it 26
into bits. He looks at the bits under glass in his lab. 38

Want a plan for your brain? You can deposit it at a 50
brain bank! 52

Series 6 — King of the Court

Pancho Gonzales grew up in the 1940s and 1950s. 9
Back then, most tennis camps and clubs were just for 19
whites. Mexican Americans like Pancho had little 26
chance to take lessons. 30

So Pancho decided to teach himself. He practiced 38
hard. He was determined to be the best. 46

Pancho became a fantastic player. He had a very rapid 56
serve. He got to the top rank in tennis. Pancho was king 68
of the court! 71

Series 7	**Something Fishy**

Vets rush to help a sick pet. They do surgery. They   11
stitch up its chest. What's the catch? This patient is just   22
a fish.   24

Some people might just flush a sick fish. Others spend   34
lots of cash on medical help. They love pet fish!   44

Series 8	**High-Flying Circus**

Check out this school. You might be shocked. This is   10
not a typical school. It's a circus school.   18

Kids do math and spelling. But the big subjects   27
are flipping and twisting. Kids practice jumping and   35
catching. They do thrilling tricks, too.   41

These kids are on the path to jobs in the circus!   52

Series 9	**Struggle for Survival**

A leopard has a problem. He lets his lunch tumble   10
from a branch. A hyena snatches it in her powerful jaws.   21
The leopard wants it back. The animals struggle.   29

A lioness brings the struggle to an end. Her size is her   41
advantage. The other animals run from her. The lioness   50
grabs the lunch in an instant.   56

Live From the Hive

Sometimes, hornets attack! They dive inside a hive. 8
They kill the bees. They take the honey. 16

How do hornets do this? First, a single hornet races to 27
the hive. It tags the hive with a special smell. Then other 39
hornets can sniff out the hive. 45

But this plan only works when the first hornet escapes 55
with its life. Sometimes, bees stage the first strike. They 65
signal each other. They surround the hornet. Then they 74
vibrate together. 76

The bees bake the hornet alive. What a punishment! 85

Hero of Hope

Emmanuel lives in Ghana. He is missing a bone in his 11
right leg. In Ghana, people like him often got rejected. 21
Some felt that they were unable to contribute. 29

Emmanuel decided to demonstrate what he could do. 37
He taught himself to ride a bike. He used just his left leg 50
to ride. He rode 379 miles across Ghana. 58

Huge crowds came to see Emmanuel ride. His 66
amazing ride changed minds about the disabled. 73
Emmanuel gave hope to disabled people. 79

Series 12	## Up and Running

Ordinary life can be challenging for kids who live **9**
in difficult places. Some teachers in California offered **17**
a bunch of kids a new kind of challenge. They invited **28**
them to run a marathon. That's a 26-mile race! **37**

Getting fit for the race was difficult. Some kids **46**
disliked it at first. They thought about quitting. But in **56**
time, they were running many miles. **62**

The day of the big race came. Fifty-four kids jogged **72**
across the finish line! That's just the beginning. **80**
What else will they do with hard work and the desire **91**
for success? **93**

Series 13	## Flies That Spy

Spy planes are huge. They fly high so no one will **11**
notice them. They take snapshots of cities below. **19**

But what if you hoped to spy inside buildings? You **29**
would need tiny planes. Luckily, engineers are trying to **38**
develop them. **40**

The new generation of planes may look like insects. **49**
Their wings will flap like flies' wings. They will whiz **59**
into buildings. They will buzz around computers and **67**
phones. They will go places big spy planes can't! **76**

Series 14 — Robots: Now It's Personal

Cynthia makes complex robots. She makes robots that behave like humans. Real human babies are the basis of her designs. She uses her baby as a model. 8 18 27

Cynthia made a robot named Leo. When she chats with him, Leo focuses on her face. He can recognize her emotions. 36 46 48

Take a moment to chat with Leo. You might forget that he is a machine! 58 63

Series 15 — Hail to the Chef

Step inside the White House kitchen. The head chef is the person who maintains it. And Cris was the first woman hired to do that job. 9 20 26

What's expected of the top chef? Every day, she makes perfect meals for powerful people. She uses her training in cooking. She manages the kitchen, too. She must stay on top of every detail. 36 45 55 60

Does that sound stressful? It is! But every detail is important when the President is waiting for a daily snack! 69 78 80

Series 16	**Going Coastal**

The city of Dubai roasts in the desert sun. But its ruler   12
had a goal. He would create a new coastal area. People   23
could go there to cool off.   29

Workers sucked up sand from below the sea. They   38
used it to form islands shaped like palm trees.   47

The Palm Islands development was made to impress   55
people. It boasts hundreds of homes, hotels, and shops.   64
It has sandy beaches for swimming and boating.   72

The price tag may impress you, too. Dubai spent tens   82
of billions to create these islands!   88

Series 17	**The Dream Team**

Aniak, Alaska, is a village deep in the Alaskan wild.   10
What happens when there is a major emergency? A   19
team of teens rushes to help. Aniak has no cash to pay   31
an adult rescue crew. So local teens agreed to be trained   42
as volunteers.   44

In the wild, victims can be difficult to reach. The   54
teens sometimes travel by truck or speedboat. They   62
might even need a plane. But this dream team can't be   73
defeated. They will do anything they can to save lives.   83

Get Ready to Roll!

New Zealand is a land of extreme sports. The latest fad 11
is a giant plastic bubble. The objective is to step inside 22
and roll. It's a wild ride! 28

Riders can use their feet to set their own pace. Or, 39
they can fold themselves inside the bubble high on a hill. 50
They get a push. Then they hang on tightly as they roll to 63
the bottom at a frightening rate! 69

The rolling sensation is catching on everywhere. Are 77
you ready to roll? 81

Shark Attack?

Something was killing the dogfish sharks in the tank 9
at the big fish exhibit. Sharks are large and have sharp 20
teeth. They are expert killers. So, what was killing them? 30
No one was certain. 34

The only other large animal in the tank was an 44
octopus. And an octopus usually eats small animals, like 53
crabs and shrimp. It was a murder mystery. 61

A camera was set up to observe the tank. It revealed 72
the octopus killing a shark. The shark murder mystery 81
was solved. 83

| Series 20 | **A Born Winner** |

Kyle was born with a rare disorder. He has no hands or feet. His limbs are very short. | 11 / 18

Despite his disorder, Kyle has never backed down from a challenge. In high school, he decided it was important to compete in a sport. Kyle chose wrestling. But could he score? | 26 / 36 / 45 / 49

Kyle trained his hardest to prepare. He developed his muscles until they were bigger than ever before. Soon, he was a top performer on his team. Kyle became a state champ and showed once more that he is a born winner! | 58 / 67 / 79 / 90

| Series 21 | **Get Down and Clown!** |

Tommy the Clown invented a dance called clowning. He performed it at birthday parties. Party crowds wanted to learn his moves. So Tommy opened a school to instruct them. He made two rules for his students. They had to avoid gangs and they had to get good grades. | 8 / 16 / 25 / 35 / 46 / 48

Soon, clowning got very popular. Kids around the nation started forming groups. Clown dancers proudly point out that clowning is powerful. It keeps kids out of gangs and in school. And it brings joy to crowds of fans! | 56 / 63 / 74 / 86

Series 22 — Pit Crew U

At Pit Crew U, students learn to service race cars. A 11
pit crew must be fast to be useful during a race. The 23
car hits the pit. Crew members grab their tools. They 33
wipe the windshield so it's spotless. They fill the tank 43
with gas. They replace the tires with new ones. In less 54
than thirteen seconds, the car is ready to zoom around 64
the track. 66

The driver is the person who will appear on the news. 77
But every driver needs a cool crew to win. 86

Series 23 — Look Out Below!

The Skywalk is a clear, U-shaped platform. It juts out 10
from the edge of the Grand Canyon. It gives visitors a 21
jaw-dropping outlook on this natural wonder. 27

Take a stroll on the platform's footpath. Gaze to the 37
bottom of the canyon. It's 4,000 feet below! 45

You might ask whether the platform is dangerous. 53
Park rangers assure visitors that there's no need for 62
extreme caution. Engineers used a million pounds of 70
steel to construct the Skywalk. It can hold 71 jumbo jets! 81
So, the Skywalk is very sturdy—but looking down might 91
inspire fright! 93

Series 24 | **Back in Action**

Technology can help make life more enjoyable for   8
amputees. For example, new materials make artificial   15
limbs flexible and light. People who use these limbs   24
can take a stroll without discomfort. Feet shaped for   33
running give athletes cause for celebration. Computer   40
chips make artificial joints highly adjustable.   46

Juan has the world's first bionic hand. First, he moves 56
his biceps. Electrodes in the hand detect the movement. 65
They send a message to the fingers. The information tells 75
the fingers what to do.   80

Technology keeps moving forward. That means   86
disabled people can keep moving forward, too.   93

Congratulations!

Dear Reader: 2

You have mastered the system! Can I get your 11
autograph? 12

On your way through the four parts of the system, 22
you have seen videos starring baby bats, tennis champs, 31
social robots, dancing clowns, and more. Today, you are 40
the star. 42

What did it take to transport yourself across the finish 52
line of this program? You needed hard work, intelligence, 61
and the perseverance to keep going—even when you felt 71
like you might never crack the code. 78

Where will you go from here? Only you can decide. 88
But I predict great things for your future! 96

Best wishes, 98

Ivan 99

Grade 5, Passage 1

Lewis and Clark

In 1803, President Thomas Jefferson bought a large piece of land from France. Then he asked a man named Meriwether Lewis to explore this land and map a new route to the Pacific Ocean.

Lewis agreed to make the trip and find out as much as he could. He knew that the trip would take more than a year, and he would need lots of help. He asked his friend, Captain William Clark, to join him. Then they put together a group of about fifty men who were familiar with the wilderness. They all agreed to take the journey west.

In 1804, Lewis and Clark's expedition began. They left St. Louis by boat in the spring and headed across the plains. They found plenty of deer, buffalo, and other game. The group also met people of several different Indian nations. In one place, Lewis and Clark met a French trader and his Indian wife. Lewis asked them to join their group because the woman could speak two Indian languages. She was also familiar with the land.

This woman was very helpful on the journey. Thanks to her, Lewis and Clark were able to speak to the Indians they met. She helped them trade for horses and other supplies. The journey would have been much more difficult without this woman's help.

The Pony Express

Today, we receive mail almost every day. Letters and packages are carried by trucks, planes, and ships. We can get packages delivered to many places overnight. However, the mail system in the United States was quite different in the past.

By 1850, the eastern states were getting crowded. People needed more land so they moved west to California and Oregon. Once they moved, they could not get up-to-date news and information. Mail often took six months or more to reach them.

Mr. William Russell thought that something needed to be done. In 1860, he began the Pony Express. He set up a route westward that was almost 2,000 miles long. He hired dozens of horseback riders. He bought hundreds of horses to make the journey. Each rider rode about one hundred miles. The horses ran at full speed, so the riders had to change their horses every ten to fifteen miles. Russell built stations for these changes to take place. He promised that his Pony Express would deliver mail to California in only ten days!

The Pony Express completed 308 mail runs and delivered almost 35,000 letters through rain, snow, and other harsh conditions. However, it lasted only eighteen months because it was too expensive to keep going.

Grade 5, Passage 3

Looking for Gold

"Come on, son, you can make it," said Josh's father.

As Josh walked up the hill, he felt tired from the three-hour hike through the dusty countryside. But he didn't dare complain to his father and older brother who were a few feet ahead of him on the trail. Thirteen-year-old Josh knew he would be one of the youngest of all the people searching for gold. He had begged his father for this chance so he couldn't complain now.

Months earlier, a pioneer had found a gold nugget in California. Father's job at the sawmill did not pay much money. He wanted his family to have a better life. So he decided to travel to California to look for gold. Father was only going to take his oldest son, but Josh had begged him to come along, too.

Josh dragged his heavy legs up the steep hill. He wondered if he had made the right choice to come here.

Suddenly, Josh's brother yelled, "Look, there's the American River down below. We've found our goldmine!"

Josh reached the top of the hill and looked down. Below were hundreds of men digging in the river, looking for gold. Josh's father whooped with joy. The threesome began to run down the hill to begin their search.

The Irish Potato Famine

Ireland is an island country located in Europe to the west of England. Today, the people and governments in Ireland and England are friendly, but this was not always the case. In earlier times, life in Ireland was very difficult.

In the past, England controlled all of Ireland. The English government did not treat the Irish people well. There were not many laws to protect the Irish from landlords who made them pay high prices to live and farm on their land. As a result, the Irish had to sell most of their vegetables and cattle in order to survive. Almost all of the wheat and oats grown in Ireland were exported to England. Irish farmers could only afford to keep their potato crop to feed their families.

In 1845 and 1846, a series of diseases hit the Irish farmers' potato crops. The diseases did not affect wheat or oats. But just about all of the potatoes were destroyed. The Irish people had no food to eat, and many died from hunger.

Many Irish people decided that they had no choice but to leave their homeland. They boarded ships and sailed to the United States. Nearly a million Irish people moved to big cities such as New York and Boston to begin new lives.

Grade 6, Passage 2

Ellis Island

In the late nineteenth century, thousands of families from countries all over Europe moved to America. Some wanted a better education for their children, while others wanted to find jobs. All of these people believed they would find better lives in America.

When these immigrants arrived on ships from Europe, they landed at Ellis Island in New York Harbor. Ellis Island was the gateway to the United States. There were thirty-five buildings on the island, including the Main Building with its Great Hall. That's where most immigrants went first. From 1892 to 1954, more than twelve million immigrants passed through the Great Hall at Ellis Island.

When immigrants arrived, they first had to wait in long lines to find out if they would be allowed to enter the country. They received medical exams to make sure they did not have diseases. They had to answer questions about where they came from, their educational backgrounds, and their job skills. Officials questioned them about how much money they had. After all the questions were answered, most immigrants were allowed into the United States. But some were sent back to their home countries.

In the next four decades, immigration to the United States slowed down considerably and Ellis Island became unnecessary. In 1954, the doors of the Great Hall closed.

A New Life

When I was eight years old, I came to the United States from El Salvador. My father had a job waiting for him at an important company in Washington, D.C. I did not know anything about Washington.

My last day of school in El Salvador was very sad because I had to say goodbye to my friends. Not only was I unhappy, but I was also very nervous about making friends in my new home. I only knew a few words of English, so how would I communicate with my classmates?

We flew on an airplane to America. My mother said we would have to buy heavy coats and warm clothes when we arrived. In El Salvador, I wore only short sleeves since the weather was always hot. My mother said the weather in Washington would be cold since it was the middle of winter. But I did not really understand what that meant. Of course I had read about winter in books, but the only time I ever felt cold was when I reached into the freezer to get some ice!

My journey began ten years ago. Today, I am happy to report that I have learned English, weathered many cold winters, and have lots of great friends. At first it was hard to adjust, but now I love my new life.

Grade 7, Passage 1

Spotted Eagle and Black Crow

Spotted Eagle and Black Crow were two warriors who loved the same girl, Red Bird. But she liked Spotted Eagle best. This made Black Crow jealous.

One day the two braves were climbing high cliffs in the mountains. At one point they looked down and saw an eagle nest on a ledge far below, and they noticed baby eagles in the nest.

"Let's bring those baby eagles home," said Black Crow.

When his companion agreed, Black Crow lowered Spotted Eagle to the ledge with a rope. Then he dropped the rope and went home. When he got back to the village, he told the people that his friend had fallen to his death.

Spotted Eagle soon realized that he had been abandoned. Luckily, the parent eagles brought plenty of food for their babies. They shared their food with the man, so he survived for weeks until the young birds could fly.

"Brothers, you have accepted me," he said to them one morning. "Now I ask one more favor." He grabbed a leg of each bird and prayed, and the eagles flew him safely to the ground.

Spotted Eagle returned to his village to find that Black Crow had married Red Bird, but he said nothing. Months later, Black Crow died in battle, and Spotted Eagle ended up marrying Red Bird after all.

A New Alphabet

Sequoyah never learned English, but this brilliant man invented a way to write his own Cherokee language. He was the only person ever to create a totally new system of writing by himself.

Sequoyah was born in a Cherokee village on the Tennessee River. He became lame while still a young boy, but despite his injury, he fought in the War of 1812. During the war, he noticed that some soldiers could write letters and read them. They could also read battle orders instead of having to memorize them. His war experience made Sequoyah curious about the written language.

For a dozen years, Sequoyah experimented with different ways of writing down the sounds of his own language. Other Indians thought he was crazy and laughed at him. He tried using pictures to stand for words and ideas, but this wasn't practical. Then he thought of using letters to stand for the eighty-five sounds that he had identified in Cherokee.

When he showed the tribal elders how his alphabet worked, they were astounded. They quickly accepted his invention, and within months many Cherokees learned to read and write their language. A newspaper began in 1827, and soon books were published in Cherokee. To this day, it remains the only written Native American language.

Grade 7, Passage 3

The Indian Sweat Lodge

When Europeans arrived in a new land, they found that many groups of Native Americans used sweat lodges. Like a sauna or a steam bath, the Indian sweat lodge is a place for cleaning, relaxing, and socializing. It also has healing and sacred uses.

The most common type of sweat lodge is the vapor bath. Stones are heated in a fire outside the lodge and brought inside. Then the lodge is sealed to hold in heat. Fragrant cedar and sweetgrass are placed on the hot stones. Then water is poured over the stones to make steam. During the sweat, people often sing, chant, and pray. Afterward, they sometimes plunge into cold water.

In earlier times, people sometimes built a lodge with willow poles and birch bark after a long day of travel. Sitting in the lodge to sweat would clean and refresh their tired bodies and spirits. Sweat lodges were used to cure illness, such as fevers and skin problems. They were also used to clear the mind and renew a person's connection to the gods.

Sweat lodges almost disappeared after 1873 when the U.S. government banned many Native American practices. In some areas, the bans were not lifted till the 1930s. Today, sweat lodges have once again become a basic part of life for many Native Americans.

A First for the Women of Nepal

If you picture a group of hikers in the high mountains of Asia, you probably see a troop of hardy men. People who hike the rugged mountains of Nepal must be strong and adventurous. But they don't have to be men.

A thirty-year-old woman named Kamala has been climbing and hiking in the mountains of Nepal for years. She has also led many groups through the mountains. Since 1999, she has worked for Empowering Women of Nepal, a group that trains women to lead these demanding treks. Kamala was very shy when she started out, but training gave her confidence and skills. Nonetheless, trading the colorful saris she used to wear for pants and hiking boots was difficult.

Kamala says that it was really hard to travel with male guides, too. Many of the male guides resented women who were taking their jobs.

Her parents raised her to be a dutiful housewife and farm worker, but Kamala was very independent. She decided to help make a different kind of society for the women of her country.

Kamala earns about three times the wages of most working women in Nepal. With that money, she and her husband can afford private school for their daughter. Kamala hopes her daughter can someday exceed her own achievements.

Grade 8, Passage 2

A Volcano Erupts

The island country of Indonesia has more than one hundred active volcanoes. One of them erupts almost every year, so Indonesians are used to their smoking and rumbling. However, some blow-ups are worse than others, and one of the worst was the eruption of Krakatoa in 1883.

On May 20 of that year, an earthquake shook the small, uninhabited island of Krakatoa. A cloud of ash and dust rose several miles above the mountain. For three months afterward, the residents of nearby islands witnessed churning black clouds and heard explosions. Some people even chartered boats to sail over and get a better view.

Then on August 27, the mountain exploded with stunning force. Searing heat flowed out over the water, killing everything in its path, including some 2,000 people. Giant tidal waves caused by the eruption took some 34,000 more lives. These enormous waves destroyed boats and wrecked coastlines for thousands of miles in every direction. For three days, thick black clouds completely blocked the sun.

When the dust cleared, two-thirds of the island was gone and there was a deep underwater crater where the mountain's peak had been. Far below the crater, a new volcano began to rumble. Some people believed it was a mountain waiting to be born.

The Woman in the Moon

An ancient myth says that long, long ago, there were ten suns that took turns rising in the morning and setting at night. One day, all ten of them rose at once, and poor Earth became an inferno. Crops baked in the fields, the rivers dried up, and the people grew desperate from hunger and thirst. The emperor of China asked a hero named Hu Yee if he could help. The brave warrior climbed a mountain, raised his miraculous bow, and shot down nine suns, one by one; he ordered the last sun to rise and set at fixed hours.

Hu Yee's reward from the emperor was a magic potion. If he shared it with his wife Chang, they would both live for eternity; but if only one of them drank it, that one would immediately ascend to Heaven and become immortal. The couple decided they would drink it together someday when the moon was full.

One day, Hu Yee was out hunting when an evil man came to steal the potion. Rather than let him have the precious drink, Chang impulsively swallowed it herself. The servants watched in awe as she floated up into the sky.

When Hu Yee returned, the servants told him what had happened, and he was overcome with grief. But that night the moon rose, and Hu Yee was quite sure that he saw his beautiful wife in the moon.

My Achievements

My Individual Learning Plan: Behavioral Goals Rubric

Responsibility

👥 Whole Group	👥 Small Group	
Arrive on time.	Transition to small group quickly and quietly.	
Bring your *44Book*, Do Now Log, and a pencil or pen.	Bring your *44Book* and a pencil or pen.	
Complete the Do Now immediately.	Begin assigned tasks immediately.	
Be prepared to answer teacher's questions.	Be prepared to answer teacher's questions.	
Points ① ② ③ ④	① ② ③ ④	

Respect

👥 Whole Group	👥 Small Group	
Listen actively with your eyes and ears.	Listen actively with your eyes and ears.	
Use kind words, polite tone, and appropriate language.	Use kind words, polite tone, and appropriate language.	
Share materials when appropriate.	Share materials when appropriate.	
Leave whole-group area clean and organized.	Leave small-group area clean and organized.	
Points ① ② ③ ④	① ② ③ ④	

Effort

👥 Whole Group	👥 Small Group	
Complete Do Now and Wrap Up with accuracy and care.	Complete *44Book* and RDI tasks with accuracy and care.	
Pay attention to directions and details.	Pay attention to directions and details.	
Ignore distractions.	Ignore distractions.	
Keep trying!	Complete My *44Book* Response Log and keep trying!	
Points ① ② ③ ④	① ② ③ ④	

Week of _____

📖 Independent Reading	💻 Software	
Transition to independent reading quickly and quietly.	Transition to your computer quickly and quietly.	
Choose a paperback, eBook, or Audiobook.	Find your designated work station.	
Begin reading immediately.	Log into your computer immediately.	
Be prepared to think and write.	Be prepared to answer the questions on the software.	**Total Points:** /16
① ② ③ ④	① ② ③ ④	

📖 Independent Reading	💻 Software	
Stay focused on your own book.	Work on the computer independently and allow others to work independently.	
Find new books without distracting others.	Use appropriate voice level when reading aloud.	
Treat books with care and use them respectfully.	Use materials (keyboard, monitor, headphones, mouse) carefully.	
Return book to designated area when you are done with it.	Leave the computer work station clean and organized.	**Total Points:** /16
① ② ③ ④	① ② ③ ④	

📖 Independent Reading	💻 Software	
Pay careful attention to your reading.	Work on the software for 15 minutes a day.	
Look up words you don't understand.	Speak clearly and naturally when reading aloud.	
Ignore distractions.	Ignore distractions.	
Complete Reading Logs and QuickWrite.	Use the dashboard and My Software Tracking Log to monitor your software and reading progress.	**Total Points:** /16
① ② ③ ④	① ② ③ ④	

Total Points: /48

My Individual Learning Plan: Behavioral Goals Rubric

Responsibility

👥 Whole Group	👥 Small Group	
Arrive on time.	Transition to small group quickly and quietly.	
Bring your *44Book*, Do Now Log, and a pencil or pen.	Bring your *44Book* and a pencil or pen.	
Complete the Do Now immediately.	Begin assigned tasks immediately.	
Be prepared to answer teacher's questions.	Be prepared to answer teacher's questions.	
Points ① ② ③ ④	① ② ③ ④	

Respect

👥 Whole Group	👥 Small Group	
Listen actively with your eyes and ears.	Listen actively with your eyes and ears.	
Use kind words, polite tone, and appropriate language.	Use kind words, polite tone, and appropriate language.	
Share materials when appropriate.	Share materials when appropriate.	
Leave whole-group area clean and organized.	Leave small-group area clean and organized.	
Points ① ② ③ ④	① ② ③ ④	

Effort

👥 Whole Group	👥 Small Group	
Complete Do Now and Wrap Up with accuracy and care.	Complete *44Book* and RDI tasks with accuracy and care.	
Pay attention to directions and details.	Pay attention to directions and details.	
Ignore distractions.	Ignore distractions.	
Keep trying!	Complete My *44Book* Response Log and keep trying!	
Points ① ② ③ ④	① ② ③ ④	

Week of _____

📖 Independent Reading	💻 Software	
Transition to independent reading quickly and quietly.	Transition to your computer quickly and quietly.	
Choose a paperback, eBook, or Audiobook.	Find your designated work station.	
Begin reading immediately.	Log into your computer immediately.	
Be prepared to think and write.	Be prepared to answer the questions on the software.	**Total Points: /16**
① ② ③ ④	① ② ③ ④	

📖 Independent Reading	💻 Software	
Stay focused on your own book.	Work on the computer independently and allow others to work independently.	
Find new books without distracting others.	Use appropriate voice level when reading aloud.	
Treat books with care and use them respectfully.	Use materials (keyboard, monitor, headphones, mouse) carefully.	
Return book to designated area when you are done with it.	Leave the computer work station clean and organized.	**Total Points: /16**
① ② ③ ④	① ② ③ ④	

📖 Independent Reading	💻 Software	
Pay careful attention to your reading.	Work on the software for 15 minutes a day.	
Look up words you don't understand.	Speak clearly and naturally when reading aloud.	
Ignore distractions.	Ignore distractions.	
Complete Reading Logs and QuickWrite.	Use the dashboard and My Software Tracking Log to monitor your software and reading progress.	**Total Points: /16**
① ② ③ ④	① ② ③ ④	

Total Points: /48

My Individual Learning Plan: Behavioral Goals Rubric

Responsibility

👥 Whole Group	👥 Small Group	
Arrive on time.	Transition to small group quickly and quietly.	
Bring your *44Book*, Do Now Log, and a pencil or pen.	Bring your *44Book* and a pencil or pen.	
Complete the Do Now immediately.	Begin assigned tasks immediately.	
Be prepared to answer teacher's questions.	Be prepared to answer teacher's questions.	
Points ① ② ③ ④	① ② ③ ④	

Respect

👥 Whole Group	👥 Small Group	
Listen actively with your eyes and ears.	Listen actively with your eyes and ears.	
Use kind words, polite tone, and appropriate language.	Use kind words, polite tone, and appropriate language.	
Share materials when appropriate.	Share materials when appropriate.	
Leave whole-group area clean and organized.	Leave small-group area clean and organized.	
Points ① ② ③ ④	① ② ③ ④	

Effort

👥 Whole Group	👥 Small Group	
Complete Do Now and Wrap Up with accuracy and care.	Complete *44Book* and RDI tasks with accuracy and care.	
Pay attention to directions and details.	Pay attention to directions and details.	
Ignore distractions.	Ignore distractions.	
Keep trying!	Complete My *44Book* Response Log and keep trying!	
Points ① ② ③ ④	① ② ③ ④	

Week of _____

📖 Independent Reading	💻 Software	
Transition to independent reading quickly and quietly.	Transition to your computer quickly and quietly.	
Choose a paperback, eBook, or Audiobook.	Find your designated work station.	
Begin reading immediately.	Log into your computer immediately.	
Be prepared to think and write.	Be prepared to answer the questions on the software.	**Total Points:** /16
① ② ③ ④	① ② ③ ④	

📖 Independent Reading	💻 Software	
Stay focused on your own book.	Work on the computer independently and allow others to work independently.	
Find new books without distracting others.	Use appropriate voice level when reading aloud.	
Treat books with care and use them respectfully.	Use materials (keyboard, monitor, headphones, mouse) carefully.	
Return book to designated area when you are done with it.	Leave the computer work station clean and organized.	**Total Points:** /16
① ② ③ ④	① ② ③ ④	

📖 Independent Reading	💻 Software	
Pay careful attention to your reading.	Work on the software for 15 minutes a day.	
Look up words you don't understand.	Speak clearly and naturally when reading aloud.	
Ignore distractions.	Ignore distractions.	
Complete Reading Logs and QuickWrite.	Use the dashboard and My Software Tracking Log to monitor your software and reading progress.	**Total Points:** /16
① ② ③ ④	① ② ③ ④	

Total Points: /48

My Individual Learning Plan: Behavioral Goals Rubric

Responsibility

👥 Whole Group	👥 Small Group	
Arrive on time.	Transition to small group quickly and quietly.	
Bring your *44Book*, Do Now Log, and a pencil or pen.	Bring your *44Book* and a pencil or pen.	
Complete the Do Now immediately.	Begin assigned tasks immediately.	
Be prepared to answer teacher's questions.	Be prepared to answer teacher's questions.	
Points ① ② ③ ④	① ② ③ ④	

Respect

👥 Whole Group	👥 Small Group	
Listen actively with your eyes and ears.	Listen actively with your eyes and ears.	
Use kind words, polite tone, and appropriate language.	Use kind words, polite tone, and appropriate language.	
Share materials when appropriate.	Share materials when appropriate.	
Leave whole-group area clean and organized.	Leave small-group area clean and organized.	
Points ① ② ③ ④	① ② ③ ④	

Effort

👥 Whole Group	👥 Small Group	
Complete Do Now and Wrap Up with accuracy and care.	Complete *44Book* and RDI tasks with accuracy and care.	
Pay attention to directions and details.	Pay attention to directions and details.	
Ignore distractions.	Ignore distractions.	
Keep trying!	Complete My *44Book* Response Log and keep trying!	
Points ① ② ③ ④	① ② ③ ④	

Week of _____

📖 Independent Reading	🖥 Software
Transition to independent reading quickly and quietly.	Transition to your computer quickly and quietly.
Choose a paperback, eBook, or Audiobook.	Find your designated work station.
Begin reading immediately.	Log into your computer immediately.
Be prepared to think and write.	Be prepared to answer the questions on the software.
① ② ③ ④	① ② ③ ④

Total Points: /16

📖 Independent Reading	🖥 Software
Stay focused on your own book.	Work on the computer independently and allow others to work independently.
Find new books without distracting others.	Use appropriate voice level when reading aloud.
Treat books with care and use them respectfully.	Use materials (keyboard, monitor, headphones, mouse) carefully.
Return book to designated area when you are done with it.	Leave the computer work station clean and organized.
① ② ③ ④	① ② ③ ④

Total Points: /16

📖 Independent Reading	🖥 Software
Pay careful attention to your reading.	Work on the software for 15 minutes a day.
Look up words you don't understand.	Speak clearly and naturally when reading aloud.
Ignore distractions.	Ignore distractions.
Complete Reading Logs and QuickWrite.	Use the dashboard and My Software Tracking Log to monitor your software and reading progress.
① ② ③ ④	① ② ③ ④

Total Points: /16

Total Points: /48

My Individual Learning Plan: Behavioral Goals Rubric

Responsibility

👥 **Whole Group**	👥 **Small Group**	
Arrive on time.	Transition to small group quickly and quietly.	
Bring your *44Book*, Do Now Log, and a pencil or pen.	Bring your *44Book* and a pencil or pen.	
Complete the Do Now immediately.	Begin assigned tasks immediately.	
Be prepared to answer teacher's questions.	Be prepared to answer teacher's questions.	
Points ① ② ③ ④	① ② ③ ④	

Respect

👥 **Whole Group**	👥 **Small Group**	
Listen actively with your eyes and ears.	Listen actively with your eyes and ears.	
Use kind words, polite tone, and appropriate language.	Use kind words, polite tone, and appropriate language.	
Share materials when appropriate.	Share materials when appropriate.	
Leave whole-group area clean and organized.	Leave small-group area clean and organized.	
Points ① ② ③ ④	① ② ③ ④	

Effort

👥 **Whole Group**	👥 **Small Group**	
Complete Do Now and Wrap Up with accuracy and care.	Complete *44Book* and RDI tasks with accuracy and care.	
Pay attention to directions and details.	Pay attention to directions and details.	
Ignore distractions.	Ignore distractions.	
Keep trying!	Complete My *44Book* Response Log and keep trying!	
Points ① ② ③ ④	① ② ③ ④	

Week of _____

📖 Independent Reading	💻 Software
Transition to independent reading quickly and quietly.	Transition to your computer quickly and quietly.
Choose a paperback, eBook, or Audiobook.	Find your designated work station.
Begin reading immediately.	Log into your computer immediately.
Be prepared to think and write.	Be prepared to answer the questions on the software.
① ② ③ ④	① ② ③ ④

Total Points: /16

📖 Independent Reading	💻 Software
Stay focused on your own book.	Work on the computer independently and allow others to work independently.
Find new books without distracting others.	Use appropriate voice level when reading aloud.
Treat books with care and use them respectfully.	Use materials (keyboard, monitor, headphones, mouse) carefully.
Return book to designated area when you are done with it.	Leave the computer work station clean and organized.
① ② ③ ④	① ② ③ ④

Total Points: /16

📖 Independent Reading	💻 Software
Pay careful attention to your reading.	Work on the software for 15 minutes a day.
Look up words you don't understand.	Speak clearly and naturally when reading aloud.
Ignore distractions.	Ignore distractions.
Complete Reading Logs and QuickWrite.	Use the dashboard and My Software Tracking Log to monitor your software and reading progress.
① ② ③ ④	① ② ③ ④

Total Points: /16

Total Points: /48

My Individual Learning Plan: Behavioral Goals Rubric

Responsibility

👥 Whole Group	👥 Small Group	
Arrive on time.	Transition to small group quickly and quietly.	
Bring your *44Book*, Do Now Log, and a pencil or pen.	Bring your *44Book* and a pencil or pen.	
Complete the Do Now immediately.	Begin assigned tasks immediately.	
Be prepared to answer teacher's questions.	Be prepared to answer teacher's questions.	
Points ① ② ③ ④	① ② ③ ④	

Respect

👥 Whole Group	👥 Small Group	
Listen actively with your eyes and ears.	Listen actively with your eyes and ears.	
Use kind words, polite tone, and appropriate language.	Use kind words, polite tone, and appropriate language.	
Share materials when appropriate.	Share materials when appropriate.	
Leave whole-group area clean and organized.	Leave small-group area clean and organized.	
Points ① ② ③ ④	① ② ③ ④	

Effort

👥 Whole Group	👥 Small Group	
Complete Do Now and Wrap Up with accuracy and care.	Complete *44Book* and RDI tasks with accuracy and care.	
Pay attention to directions and details.	Pay attention to directions and details.	
Ignore distractions.	Ignore distractions.	
Keep trying!	Complete My *44Book* Response Log and keep trying!	
Points ① ② ③ ④	① ② ③ ④	

Week of _____

📖 Independent Reading	💻 Software
Transition to independent reading quickly and quietly.	Transition to your computer quickly and quietly.
Choose a paperback, eBook, or Audiobook.	Find your designated work station.
Begin reading immediately.	Log into your computer immediately.
Be prepared to think and write.	Be prepared to answer the questions on the software.
① ② ③ ④	① ② ③ ④

Total Points: /16

📖 Independent Reading	💻 Software
Stay focused on your own book.	Work on the computer independently and allow others to work independently.
Find new books without distracting others.	Use appropriate voice level when reading aloud.
Treat books with care and use them respectfully.	Use materials (keyboard, monitor, headphones, mouse) carefully.
Return book to designated area when you are done with it.	Leave the computer work station clean and organized.
① ② ③ ④	① ② ③ ④

Total Points: /16

📖 Independent Reading	💻 Software
Pay careful attention to your reading.	Work on the software for 15 minutes a day.
Look up words you don't understand.	Speak clearly and naturally when reading aloud.
Ignore distractions.	Ignore distractions.
Complete Reading Logs and QuickWrite.	Use the dashboard and My Software Tracking Log to monitor your software and reading progress.
① ② ③ ④	① ② ③ ④

Total Points: /16

Total Points: /48

My Individual Learning Plan: Behavioral Goals Rubric

Responsibility

👥 Whole Group	👥 Small Group	
Arrive on time.	Transition to small group quickly and quietly.	
Bring your *44Book*, Do Now Log, and a pencil or pen.	Bring your *44Book* and a pencil or pen.	
Complete the Do Now immediately.	Begin assigned tasks immediately.	
Be prepared to answer teacher's questions.	Be prepared to answer teacher's questions.	
Points ① ② ③ ④	① ② ③ ④	

Respect

👥 Whole Group	👥 Small Group	
Listen actively with your eyes and ears.	Listen actively with your eyes and ears.	
Use kind words, polite tone, and appropriate language.	Use kind words, polite tone, and appropriate language.	
Share materials when appropriate.	Share materials when appropriate.	
Leave whole-group area clean and organized.	Leave small-group area clean and organized.	
Points ① ② ③ ④	① ② ③ ④	

Effort

👥 Whole Group	👥 Small Group	
Complete Do Now and Wrap Up with accuracy and care.	Complete *44Book* and RDI tasks with accuracy and care.	
Pay attention to directions and details.	Pay attention to directions and details.	
Ignore distractions.	Ignore distractions.	
Keep trying!	Complete My *44Book* Response Log and keep trying!	
Points ① ② ③ ④	① ② ③ ④	

Week of _____

📖 Independent Reading	💻 Software	
Transition to independent reading quickly and quietly.	Transition to your computer quickly and quietly.	
Choose a paperback, eBook, or Audiobook.	Find your designated work station.	
Begin reading immediately.	Log into your computer immediately.	
Be prepared to think and write.	Be prepared to answer the questions on the software.	**Total Points:** /16
① ② ③ ④	① ② ③ ④	

📖 Independent Reading	💻 Software	
Stay focused on your own book.	Work on the computer independently and allow others to work independently.	
Find new books without distracting others.	Use appropriate voice level when reading aloud.	
Treat books with care and use them respectfully.	Use materials (keyboard, monitor, headphones, mouse) carefully.	
Return book to designated area when you are done with it.	Leave the computer work station clean and organized.	**Total Points:** /16
① ② ③ ④	① ② ③ ④	

📖 Independent Reading	💻 Software	
Pay careful attention to your reading.	Work on the software for 15 minutes a day.	
Look up words you don't understand.	Speak clearly and naturally when reading aloud.	
Ignore distractions.	Ignore distractions.	
Complete Reading Logs and QuickWrite.	Use the dashboard and My Software Tracking Log to monitor your software and reading progress.	**Total Points:** /16
① ② ③ ④	① ② ③ ④	

Total Points:	**/48**

My Individual Learning Plan: Academic Goals

Suggested action steps to accomplish goals.

Decoding Annual Goal

1. Try my best during software activities.
2. Listen to instructions again if I am confused.
3. Click the Word or Sentence button if I need to hear it again.
4. Answer as quickly and carefully as I can.

Spelling Annual Goal

1. Try my best during the spelling activities.
2. Think about the spelling rules I am learning before I type a word.
3. Reread what word I spelled before I click Enter.
4. Be careful about which words I capitalize.
5. Click the Word or Sentence button if I need to hear it again.

Comprehension Annual Goal

1. Select a book based on my software progress.
2. Read each book more than one time.
3. Carefully complete my reading response logs.

Sample

By (date) _November 15,_ I plan to _complete 10 software topics._ To accomplish this goal, I need to _try my best during software activities._

1. Decoding	Annual Goal
	I will score at least 70% on my software progress monitors for 160 software topics.

Conference 1

By (date) _____, I plan to _____ To accomplish this goal,

I need to _____

Conference 2

By (date) _____, I plan to _____ To accomplish this goal,

I need to _____

Conference 3

By (date) _____, I plan to _____ To accomplish this goal,

I need to _____

Conference 4

By (date) _____, I plan to _____ To accomplish this goal,

I need to _____

2. Spelling

Annual Goal

I will score at least 70% on 133 Spelling Challenges on the software.

Conference 1

By (date) _____, I plan to _____ To accomplish this goal,

I need to _____

Conference 2

By (date) _____, I plan to _____ To accomplish this goal,

I need to _____

Conference 3

By (date) _____, I plan to _____ To accomplish this goal,

I need to _____

Conference 4

By (date) _____, I plan to _____ To accomplish this goal,

I need to _____

3. Comprehension

Annual Goal

I will read _____ books and demonstrate that I understand the key ideas by passing *Reading Counts!* quizzes.

Conference 1

By (date) _____, I plan to _____ To accomplish this goal,

I need to _____

Conference 2

By (date) _____, I plan to _____ To accomplish this goal,

I need to _____

Conference 3

By (date) _____, I plan to _____ To accomplish this goal,

I need to _____

Conference 4

By (date) _____, I plan to _____ To accomplish this goal,

I need to _____

My Conferences

Complete the information each time you conference with your teacher.
★Star one item you are proud of. Circle one item you want to improve.

CONFERENCE 1

Date: _____ Current Topic: _____

Words Read: _____ Median Session Time: _____

Decoding Fluency Score: _____ *Reading Counts!* Average Quiz Score: _____

Small-Group Participation: _____

Discuss Academic Goals

	My Goal	**Actual**
Decoding	_____ Topics Completed	_____ Topics Completed
Spelling	_____ Spelling Challenge	_____ Spelling Challenge
Comprehension	_____ Books Read	_____ Books Read

Celebrate Success

I am proud of _____

I have done well in this part of *System 44* because _____

_____

Reflect

I am struggling with _____

This is challenging because _____

Teacher Comments: _____

_____

CONFERENCE 2

Date: _____ Current Topic: _____

Words Read: _____ Median Session Time: _____

Decoding Fluency Score: _____ *Reading Counts!* Average Quiz Score: _____

Small-Group Participation: _____

Discuss Academic Goals

	My Goal	**Actual**
Decoding	_____ Topics Completed	_____ Topics Completed
Spelling	_____ Spelling Challenge	_____ Spelling Challenge
Comprehension	_____ Books Read	_____ Books Read

Celebrate Success

I am proud of _____

I have done well in this part of *System 44* because _____

_____

Reflect

I am struggling with _____

This is challenging because _____

Teacher Comments: _____

_____

CONFERENCE 3

Date: _____ Current Topic: _____

Words Read: _____ Median Session Time: _____

Decoding Fluency Score: _____ *Reading Counts!* Average Quiz Score: _____

Small-Group Participation: _____

Discuss Academic Goals

	My Goal	**Actual**
Decoding	_____ Topics Completed	_____ Topics Completed
Spelling	_____ Spelling Challenge	_____ Spelling Challenge
Comprehension	_____ Books Read	_____ Books Read

Celebrate Success

I am proud of _____

I have done well in this part of *System 44* because _____

_____

Reflect

I am struggling with _____

This is challenging because _____

Teacher Comments: _____

_____

CONFERENCE 4

Date: _____ Current Topic: _____

Words Read: _____ Median Session Time: _____

Decoding Fluency Score: _____ *Reading Counts!* Average Quiz Score: _____

Small-Group Participation: _____

Discuss Academic Goals

	My Goal	**Actual**
Decoding	_____ Topics Completed	_____ Topics Completed
Spelling	_____ Spelling Challenge	_____ Spelling Challenge
Comprehension	_____ Books Read	_____ Books Read

Celebrate Success

I am proud of _____

I have done well in this part of *System 44* because _____

_____

Reflect

I am struggling with _____

This is challenging because _____

Teacher Comments: _____

_____

SOFTWARE

My Software Tracking Log

Place a sticker on the chart below each time you complete a topic. Use your
Fast Track stickers when you fast track!

1	2	3	4	5	6	7	8	9	10	11	12	13
1.1	2.1	3.1	4.1	5.1	6.1	7.1	8.1	9.1	10.1	11.1	12.1	13.1
1.2	2.2	3.2	4.2	5.2	6.2	7.2	8.2	9.2	10.2	11.2	12.2	13.2
1.3	2.3	3.3	4.3	5.3	6.3	7.3	8.3	9.3	10.3	11.3	12.3	13.3
1.4	2.4	3.4	4.4	5.4	6.4	7.4	8.4	9.4	10.4	11.4	12.4	13.4
1.5	2.5	3.5	4.5	5.5	6.5	7.5	8.5	9.5	10.5	11.5	12.5	13.5
1.6	2.6	3.6	4.6	5.6	6.6	7.6	8.6	9.6	10.6	11.6	12.6	13.6
1.7	2.7	3.7				7.7	8.7		10.7	11.7		
1.8	2.8	3.8					8.8		10.8			

14	15	16	17	18	19	20	21	22	23	24	25
14.1	15.1	16.1	17.1	18.1	19.1	20.1	21.1	22.1	23.1	24.1	25.1
14.2	15.2	16.2	17.2	18.2	19.2	20.2	21.2	22.2	23.2	24.2	25.2
14.3	15.3	16.3	17.3	18.3	19.3	20.3	21.3	22.3	23.3	24.3	25.3
14.4	15.4	16.4	17.4	18.4	19.4	20.4	21.4	22.4	23.4	24.4	25.4
14.5	15.5	16.5	17.5	18.5	19.5	20.5	21.5	22.5	23.5	24.5	25.5
14.6			17.6		19.6	20.6	21.6			24.6	
14.7			17.7		19.7	20.7					

My Success Reads

Each time you read a Success passage, write down the date and the number of seconds it takes. Build your fluency.

Series	1st Read		2nd Read		3rd Read	
	Date	Seconds	Date	Seconds	Date	Seconds
1. *Bats Do That?* **Words:** 30						
2. *Art for Kicks* **Words:** 37						
3. *Run, Jesse, Run* **Words:** 58						
4. *Passing the Sniff Test* **Words:** 30						
5. *Brain Freeze* **Words:** 52						
6. *King of the Court* **Words:** 71						
7. *Something Fishy* **Words:** 44						
8. *High-Flying Circus* **Words:** 52						
9. *Struggle for Survival* **Words:** 56						
10. *Live From the Hive* **Words:** 85						
11. *Hero of Hope* **Words:** 79						
12. *Up and Running* **Words:** 93						
13. *Flies That Spy* **Words:** 76						

Series	1st Read		2nd Read		3rd Read	
	Date	Seconds	Date	Seconds	Date	Seconds
14. *Robots: Now It's Personal* **Words:** 63						
15. *Hail to the Chef* **Words:** 80						
16. *Going Coastal* **Words:** 88						
17. *The Dream Team* **Words:** 83						
18. *Get Ready to Roll!* **Words:** 81						
19. *Shark Attack?* **Words:** 83						
20. *A Born Winner* **Words:** 90						
21. *Get Down and Clown!* **Words:** 86						
22. *Pit Crew U* **Words:** 86						
23. *Look Out Below!* **Words:** 93						
24. *Back in Action* **Words:** 93						
25. *Congratulations!* **Words:** 99						

My Success Response Log

Keep track of the Success Series you have completed. Write the date that you finished the series. Then complete the sentence starter for each Success topic.

Series 1 — **Bats Do That?**

Date Completed: _____

In *Bats Do That?*, I learned _____

_____

_____

Series 2 — **Art for Kicks**

Date Completed: _____

Art for Kicks is about _____

_____

_____

Series 3 — **Run, Jesse, Run**

Date Completed: _____

In *Run, Jesse, Run*, Jesse Owens _____

_____

_____

Series 4 — **Passing the Sniff Test**

Date Completed: _____

Passing the Sniff Test is about dogs that _____

_____

_____

Series 5 — *Brain Freeze*

Date Completed: _____

Brain scientists in *Brain Freeze* _____

_____

_____

Series 6 — *King of the Court*

Date Completed: _____

In *King of the Court*, Pancho Gonzales _____

_____

_____

Series 7 — *Something Fishy*

Date Completed: _____

Something Fishy is about _____

_____

_____

Series 8 — *High-Flying Circus*

Date Completed: _____

The school in *High-Flying Circus* is special because _____

_____

_____

Series 9	**Struggle for Survival**

Date Completed: _____

Struggle for Survival is about _____

_____

_____

Series 10	**Live From the Hive**

Date Completed: _____

In *Live From the Hive*, I learned _____

_____

_____

Series 11	**Hero of Hope**

Date Completed: _____

In *Hero of Hope*, Emmanuel _____

_____

_____

Series 12	**Up and Running**

Date Completed: _____

Up and Running is about kids who _____

_____

_____

Series 13	**Flies That Spy**

Date Completed: _____

In *Flies That Spy*, engineers are _____

_____

_____

Series 14	**Robots: Now It's Personal**

Date Completed: _____

In *Robots: Now It's Personal*, Cynthia _____

_____

_____

Series 15	**Hail to the Chef**

Date Completed: _____

Hail to the Chef is about _____

_____

_____

Series 16	**Going Coastal**

Date Completed: _____

In *Going Coastal*, I learned _____

_____

_____

Series 17 | ***The Dream Team***

Date Completed: _____

The Dream Team is about teens in Alaska who _____

_____

_____

Series 18 | ***Get Ready to Roll!***

Date Completed: _____

Get Ready to Roll! is about _____

_____

_____

Series 19 | ***Shark Attack?***

Date Completed: _____

In *Shark Attack?*, I discovered _____

_____

_____

Series 20 | ***A Born Winner***

Date Completed: _____

In *A Born Winner*, Kyle _____

_____

_____

Series 21	**Get Down and Clown!**

Date Completed: _____

Get Down and Clown! is about _____

_____

Series 22	**Pit Crew U**

Date Completed: _____

Pit Crew U is a special school for _____

_____

Series 23	**Look Out Below!**

Date Completed: _____

In *Look Out Below!*, I learned _____

_____

Series 24	**Back in Action**

Date Completed: _____

In *Back in Action*, technology _____

_____

Series 25	**Congratulations!**

Date Completed: _____

For my future, I predict _____

_____

My Independent Reading Tracking Log

Use this chart to keep track of the books you read.

Title	Reading #				Reading Counts! Quiz Passed	Graphic Organizer Completed	QuickWrite Completed	Teacher's Initials
	1	2	3	4				

Title	Reading #				Reading Counts! Quiz Passed	Graphic Organizer Completed	QuickWrite Completed	Teacher's Initials
	1	2	3	4				

My Independent Reading Response Log

Book Title: _Weird Sports Records_

Phonics Focus: _sh, ch, -tch_

S.M.A.R.T. WORDS Date Completed: _2/22_

Write each S.M.A.R.T. Word and rate it. Then, write a sentence that uses each word.

Word	Sentence
1. error [1] [2] [☒] [4]	I only made one error on the test.
2. etiquette [☒] [2] [3] [4]	Being polite to other players is good sports etiquette.
3. exercise [1] [2] [3] [☒]	I exercise when I play soccer.
4. fine [1] [☒] [3] [4]	You will have to pay a fine if you park illegally.
5. foul [1] [2] [☒] [4]	Some sports fouls are for bad behavior.

DURING READING Date Completed: _2/23_

Answer each question on the line below:

1. (page #_5_) The loss is big because Samoa lost by 31 goals. That is a lot. Samoa did not score at all.

2. (page #_7_) "Hall of Shame" is a place where people are famous for bad behavior. Wallace's record is in the "Hall of Shame" because he earned it for acting badly on the basketball court.

3. (page #_15_) Surfing dogs and racing snails are "weird and wacky" because they are unusual!

AFTER READING
Date Completed: 2/26

Use the sentence starters to write your answer to the questions.

1. One "weird" sports record is Dwight Howard's crazy long shot.

_____

_____

2. This record is unusual because Howard made the shot while he was sitting down.

_____

_____

Date Completed: 2/28

Answer the reread question here:

Some records are weird because they are for being bad at a sport.
Some records are weird because the person was very young or very old
for the sport.

WRAP-UP

Rate this book by coloring in the number of stars:

★ ★ ★ ☆ ☆

My Reading Counts Quiz Score: 90%

TEACHER FEEDBACK

Date Completed: 3/1

My Independent Reading Response Log

Book Title: _____

Phonics Focus: _____

S.M.A.R.T. WORDS   Date Completed: _____

Write each S.M.A.R.T. Word and rate it. Then, write a sentence that uses each word.

Word	Sentence
1. 1 2 3 4	
2. 1 2 3 4	
3. 1 2 3 4	
4. 1 2 3 4	
5. 1 2 3 4	

DURING READING   Date Completed: _____

Answer each question on the line below:

1. (page #_____) _____

_____

_____

2. (page #_____) _____

_____

_____

3. (page #_____) _____

_____

_____

AFTER READING   Date Completed: _____

Use the sentence starters to write your answer to the questions.

1. _____

_____

_____

2. _____

_____

_____

Date Completed: _____

Answer the reread question here:

_____

_____

_____

WRAP-UP

Rate this book by coloring in the number of stars:

☆ ☆ ☆ ☆ ☆

My Reading Counts Quiz Score: _____

TEACHER FEEDBACK

Date Completed: _____

My Independent Reading Response Log

Book Title: _____

Phonics Focus: _____

S.M.A.R.T. WORDS   Date Completed: _____

Write each S.M.A.R.T. Word and rate it. Then, write a sentence that uses each word.

Word	Sentence
1. ☐1 ☐2 ☐3 ☐4	
2. ☐1 ☐2 ☐3 ☐4	
3. ☐1 ☐2 ☐3 ☐4	
4. ☐1 ☐2 ☐3 ☐4	
5. ☐1 ☐2 ☐3 ☐4	

DURING READING   Date Completed: _____

Answer each question on the line below:

1. (page #_____) _____

_____

_____

2. (page #_____) _____

_____

_____

3. (page #_____) _____

_____

AFTER READING   Date Completed: _____

Use the sentence starters to write your answer to the questions.

1. _____

_____

_____

2. _____

_____

_____

Date Completed: _____

Answer the reread question here:

_____

_____

_____

WRAP-UP

Rate this book by coloring in the number of stars:

☆ ☆ ☆ ☆ ☆

My Reading Counts Quiz Score: _____

TEACHER FEEDBACK

Date Completed: _____

My Independent Reading Response Log

Book Title: _____

Phonics Focus: _____

S.M.A.R.T. WORDS   Date Completed: _____

Write each S.M.A.R.T. Word and rate it. Then, write a sentence that uses each word.

Word	Sentence
1. [1] [2] [3] [4]	
2. [1] [2] [3] [4]	
3. [1] [2] [3] [4]	
4. [1] [2] [3] [4]	
5. [1] [2] [3] [4]	

DURING READING   Date Completed: _____

Answer each question on the line below:

1. (page #_____) _____

_____

_____

2. (page #_____) _____

_____

_____

3. (page #_____) _____

_____

_____

AFTER READING   Date Completed: _____

Use the sentence starters to write your answer to the questions.

1. _____

_____

_____

2. _____

_____

_____

Date Completed: _____

Answer the reread question here:

_____

_____

_____

WRAP-UP

Rate this book by coloring in the number of stars:

☆ ☆ ☆ ☆ ☆

My Reading Counts Quiz Score: _____

TEACHER FEEDBACK

Date Completed: _____

My Independent Reading Response Log

Book Title: _____

Phonics Focus: _____

S.M.A.R.T. WORDS   Date Completed: _____

Write each S.M.A.R.T. Word and rate it. Then, write a sentence that uses each word.

Word	Sentence
1. [1] [2] [3] [4]	
2. [1] [2] [3] [4]	
3. [1] [2] [3] [4]	
4. [1] [2] [3] [4]	
5. [1] [2] [3] [4]	

DURING READING   Date Completed: _____

Answer each question on the line below:

1. (page #_____) _____

_____

_____

2. (page #_____) _____

_____

_____

3. (page #_____) _____

_____

AFTER READING   Date Completed: _____

Use the sentence starters to write your answer to the questions.

1. _____

_____

_____

2. _____

_____

_____

                                     Date Completed: _____

Answer the reread question here:

_____

_____

_____

WRAP-UP

Rate this book by coloring in the number of stars:

☆　☆　☆　☆　☆

My Reading Counts Quiz Score: _____

TEACHER FEEDBACK

                                     Date Completed: _____

My Independent Reading Response Log

Book Title: _____

Phonics Focus: _____

S.M.A.R.T. WORDS   Date Completed: _____

Write each S.M.A.R.T. Word and rate it. Then, write a sentence that uses each word.

Word	Sentence
1. ☐1 ☐2 ☐3 ☐4	
2. ☐1 ☐2 ☐3 ☐4	
3. ☐1 ☐2 ☐3 ☐4	
4. ☐1 ☐2 ☐3 ☐4	
5. ☐1 ☐2 ☐3 ☐4	

DURING READING   Date Completed: _____

Answer each question on the line below:

1. (page #_____) _____

_____

_____

2. (page #_____) _____

_____

_____

3. (page #_____) _____

_____

AFTER READING

Date Completed: _____

Use the sentence starters to write your answer to the questions.

1. _____

_____

_____

2. _____

_____

_____

Date Completed: _____

Answer the reread question here:

_____

_____

_____

WRAP-UP

Rate this book by coloring in the number of stars:

☆ ☆ ☆ ☆ ☆

My Reading Counts Quiz Score: _____

TEACHER FEEDBACK

Date Completed: _____

My Decodable Digest Response Log

Follow these steps to complete the Decodable Digest Routine.

1. Read the passage independently.
2. Reread the passage with your partner or group.
3. Record passage title, genre, and page number in the response log below.
4. In the log, record the targeted element from the green band at the top left. Then, record the pattern words.
5. Answer the React question and share your response.

Write your Decodable Digest titles and responses below.

Passage Title: _____ Genre: _____

Page Number: _____

Targeted Element: _____

Pattern Words:

1: _____ 6: _____

2: _____ 7: _____

3: _____ 8: _____

4: _____ 9: _____

5: _____ 10: _____

React Question Response: _____

_____

_____

_____

_____

_____

Passage Title: _____ Genre: _____

Page Number: _____

Targeted Element: _____

Pattern Words:

1: _____   6: _____

2: _____   7: _____

3: _____   8: _____

4: _____   9: _____

5: _____   10: _____

React Question Response: _____

_____

_____

_____

_____

_____

_____

Passage Title: _____ Genre: _____

Page Number: _____

Targeted Element: _____

Pattern Words:

1: _____ 6: _____

2: _____ 7: _____

3: _____ 8: _____

4: _____ 9: _____

5: _____ 10: _____

React Question Response: _____

_____

_____

_____

_____

_____

_____

Passage Title: _____ Genre: _____

Page Number: _____

Targeted Element: _____

Pattern Words:

1: _____ 6: _____

2: _____ 7: _____

3: _____ 8: _____

4: _____ 9: _____

5: _____ 10: _____

React Question Response: _____

_____

_____

_____

_____

_____

_____

Passage Title: _____   Genre: _____

Page Number: _____

Targeted Element: _____

Pattern Words:

1: _____   6: _____

2: _____   7: _____

3: _____   8: _____

4: _____   9: _____

5: _____   10: _____

React Question Response: _____

_____

_____

_____

_____

_____

_____

Passage Title: _____ Genre: _____

Page Number: _____

Targeted Element: _____

Pattern Words:

1: _____   6: _____

2: _____   7: _____

3: _____   8: _____

4: _____   9: _____

5: _____   10: _____

React Question Response: _____

_____

_____

_____

_____

_____

_____

My *44Book* Response Log

Fill in the dates as you start and complete each Module.
Rate your effort on the Module using the Rating Scale.
Then answer a final question.

Rating Scale

needs improvement	1
average	2
good	3
excellent	4

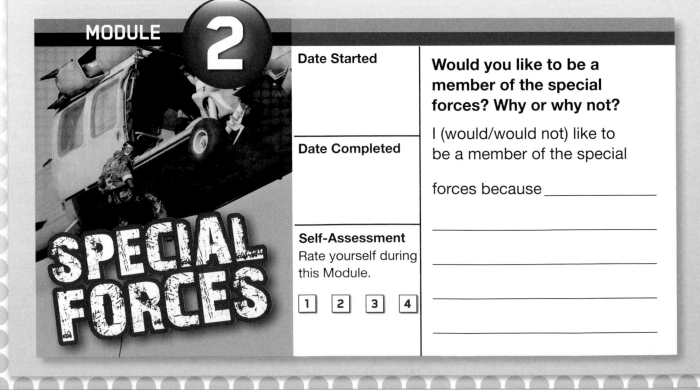

MODULE 1

SCHOOL MATTERS

Date Started

Date Completed

Self-Assessment
Rate yourself during this Module.

1　2　3　4

What is one of your academic goals?

One of my academic goals is to

_____

_____

_____

_____

_____

_____

MODULE 2

SPECIAL FORCES

Date Started

Date Completed

Self-Assessment
Rate yourself during this Module.

1　2　3　4

Would you like to be a member of the special forces? Why or why not?

I (would/would not) like to be a member of the special

forces because _____

_____

_____

_____

_____

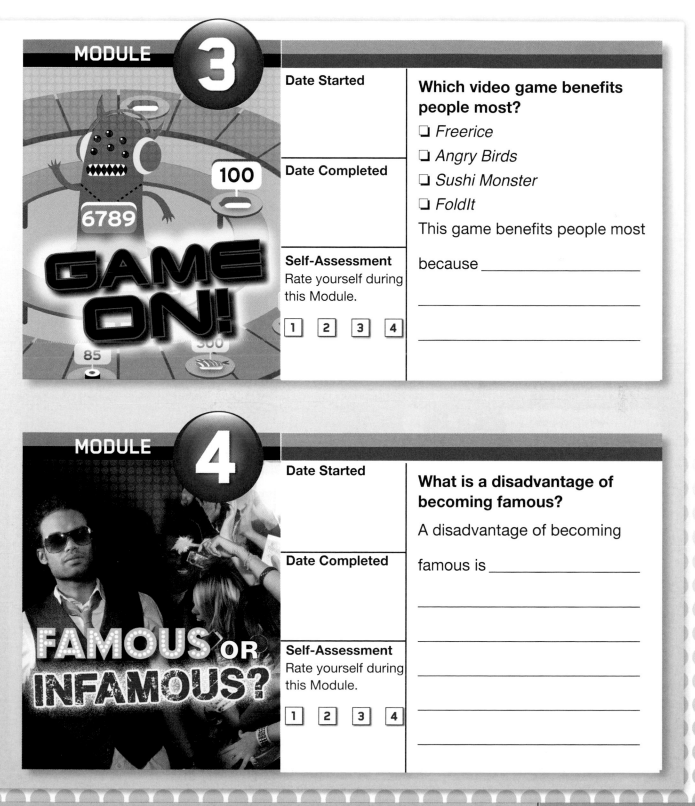

MODULE 3

GAME ON!

6789   100   85

Date Started	**Which video game benefits people most?**
	❏ *Freerice*
	❏ *Angry Birds*
Date Completed	❏ *Sushi Monster*
	❏ *FoldIt*
	This game benefits people most
Self-Assessment Rate yourself during this Module.	because _____
1 2 3 4	_____
	_____

MODULE 4

FAMOUS OR INFAMOUS?

Date Started	**What is a disadvantage of becoming famous?**
	A disadvantage of becoming
Date Completed	famous is _____
	_____
	_____
Self-Assessment Rate yourself during this Module.	_____
1 2 3 4	_____
	_____
	_____

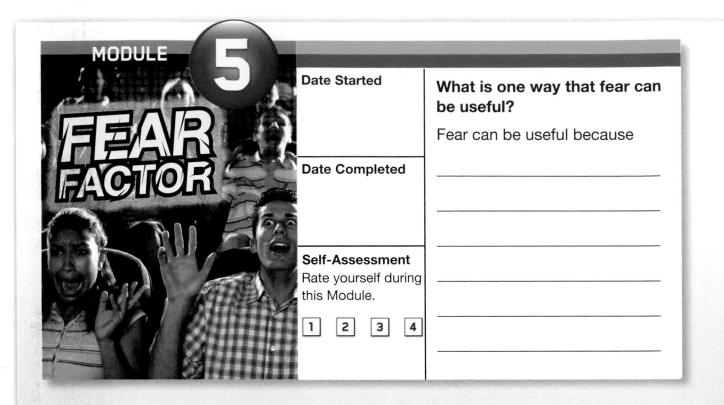

MODULE 5

FEAR FACTOR

Date Started

Date Completed

Self-Assessment
Rate yourself during this Module.

1   2   3   4

What is one way that fear can be useful?

Fear can be useful because

_____

_____

_____

_____

_____

_____

MODULE 6

GUILTY UNTIL PROVEN INNOCENT

PC JAIL

Date Started

Date Completed

Self-Assessment
Rate yourself during this Module.

1   2   3   4

What is the most interesting fact you learned in this module?

The most interesting fact I learned in this module is that

_____

_____

_____

_____

_____

MODULE 7

LOSING THEIR MINDS?

Date Started

Date Completed

Self-Assessment
Rate yourself during this Module.

| 1 | 2 | 3 | 4 |

What advice would you give to a high school football player?

_____

_____

_____

_____

_____

_____

_____

MODULE 8

Refugee Life: Starting Over

Date Started

Date Completed

Self-Assessment
Rate yourself during this Module.

| 1 | 2 | 3 | 4 |

Whose story do you find most inspiring? Why?

❑ Bala Diyali
❑ Lucy Kayee
❑ Omar Fidow

_____

_____

_____

_____

_____

My *Phonics Inventory* Progress

Create a bar graph showing your *Phonics Inventory* fluency scores over the year. Set goals for improving your decoding status.

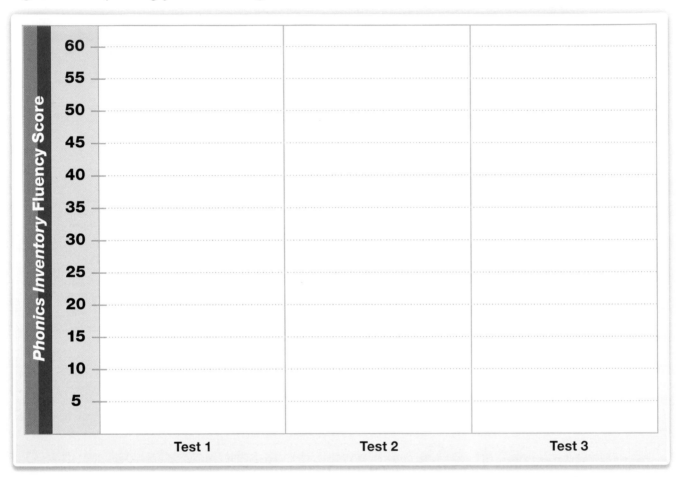

Test Date:	Test Date:	Test Date:
Fluency Score:	Fluency Score:	Fluency Score:
Decoding Status:	Decoding Status:	Decoding Status:

My *Reading Inventory* Progress

Create a bar graph showing your *Reading Inventory* Lexile® scores. Set goals for improving your reading level.

Reading Inventory Score		
1400L		
1300L		
1200L		
1100L		
1000L		
900L		
800L		
700L		
600L		
500L		
400L		
300L		
200L		
BR		

Test Date:
_____

Test Score:
_____

Test Date:
_____

Test Score:
_____

Lexile Gain:
_____

My *Reading Counts!* Progress Chart

Write the title and date that you finished your book. Then enter your score for each *Reading Counts!* quiz. Fill in one box for every correct answer.

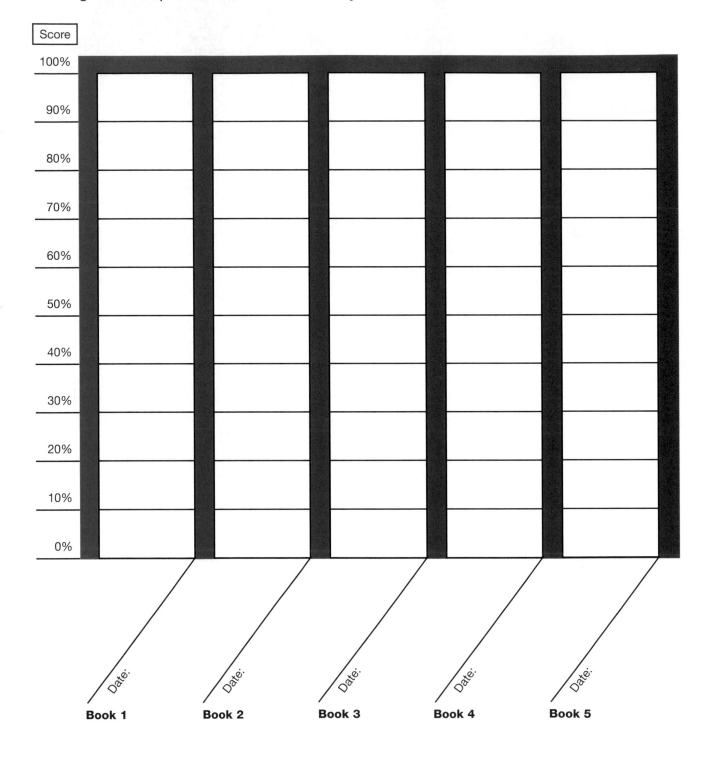

My OFA Tracking Log

After your teacher checks your oral fluency, use this chart to track your Words Correct Per Minute (WCPM).

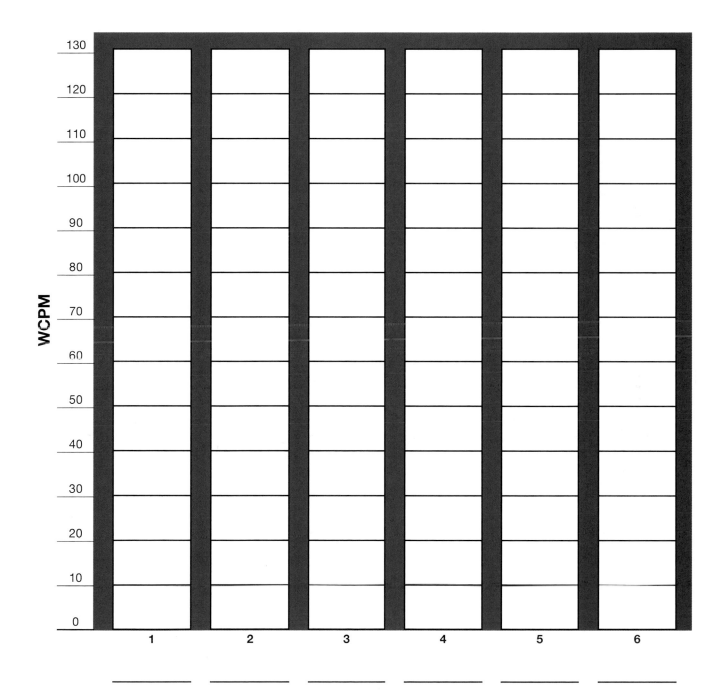

Oral Fluency Assessment Date

Small-Group Jobs

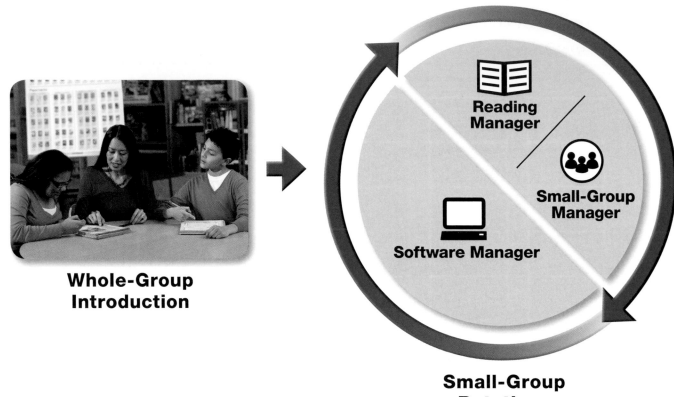

Whole-Group Introduction

Reading Manager

Small-Group Manager

Software Manager

Small-Group Rotations

Reading Manager

1. Help your group members find their books.

2. Make sure everyone fills out the reading logs during the two-minute warning.

3. Make sure the reading area is organized before moving to the next rotation.

Group Name: _____

Student: _____

Group Name: _____

Student: _____

💻 Software Manager

1. Help your group log on to the software.

2. If someone has a computer issue, help them troubleshoot. Restart the computer if necessary.

3. If you cannot help fix the computer issue, talk to the teacher.

4. Make sure the software area is organized before moving to the next rotation.

Group Name: _____

Student: _____

Group Name: _____

Student: _____

👥 Small-Group Manager

1. Hand out all materials to each group member.

2. Partner with students who missed yesterday's lesson and help answer questions.

3. Make sure the small-group area is organized before moving to the next rotation.

Group Name: _____

Student: _____

Group Name: _____

Student: _____

Other Jobs

_____

_____

_____

_____

My New Vocabulary Log

Keep track of new words you come across in your reading. For each word, write the meaning and an example that uses the word. If you can, draw a picture that will help you remember what the word means.

NEW WORD	MEANING	EXAMPLE	PICTURE

My Dictation

Write the sounds, words, or sentences you hear.

Sounds

1: _____ 3: _____ 5: _____

2: _____ 4: _____ 6: _____

Words

1: _____ 4: _____ 7: _____

2: _____ 5: _____ 8: _____

3: _____ 6: _____ 9: _____

Sentences

1. _____

_____

2. _____

_____

3. _____

_____

4. _____

_____

5. _____

_____

Six Syllable Types

1 Closed Syllable

A closed syllable ends in a consonant. It usually has a short vowel sound.

a. **hun • dred**
b. **fan • tas • tic**
c. **traf • fic**

2 Consonant + -le, -el, or -al

The consonant + -le, -el, or -al pattern usually forms its own syllable. You can split a word with the consonant + -le, -el, or -al pattern before the consonant to make it easier to read.

a. **an • gle**
b. **tun • nel**
c. **sig • nal**

3 VCe Syllable

Syllables with the vowel-consonant-e pattern (VCe) have a long vowel sound. When you split a word with this pattern into syllables, keep the letters of the VCe pattern together.

a. **on • line**
b. **com • pute**
c. **base • ment**

4 Open Syllable

An open syllable ends in a vowel. It usually has a long vowel sound.

a. **ca • ble**
b. **le • gal**
c. **mu • sic**

5 Vowel Team Syllable

When you split a word with a vowel team, keep the letters of the vowel team in the same syllable.

a. **con • tain**
b. **rea • son**
c. **dis • count**
d. **free • dom**

6 r-Controlled Vowel Syllable

When the letter r follows a vowel, the r can change the sound the vowel stands for.

a. **a • part • ment**
b. **per • son**
c. **re • turn**
d. **thirst • y**

Word Attack Strategy

1. **Look**
2. **Spot**
3. **Split**
4. **Read**

Using the Strategy

Strategy Step	Examples	
1 **Look** for any prefixes, suffixes, or endings you know. • Remember, the spelling of the base word may have changed when the ending or suffix was added.	admitted admit(t) • <u>ed</u>	undefeated <u>un</u> • defeat • <u>ed</u>
2 **Spot** the vowels in the base word. The number of vowel spots tells the number of syllables. • Remember, some vowel sounds are spelled with more than one letter.	**a**dmit(t) • ed	un • d**e**f**ea**t • ed
3 **Split** the word into syllables. • A good place to split a word is between two consonants. • If there is only one consonant between syllables, try splitting after it. • If the word doesn't sound right, try moving the split backward or forward by one letter.	a<u>d</u> • <u>m</u>it(t) • ed	~~un • def • eat • ed~~ un • d<u>e</u> • f<u>ea</u>t • ed
4 **Read** the word. Does it make a real word? If it does not, try again. • You may need to experiment with pronouncing the vowel sound differently.	admitted	undefeated

Affixes

Prefix

A word part added at the beginning of a base word to change its meaning.

Prefix	Meaning	Example
un-	not or opposite of	unlock
non-	not or opposite of	nonslip
de-	opposite of	defrost
com-	with	combine
con-	with	consist
re-	again	rewrite
pre-	before	pretest
mid-	in the middle of	midtown
sub-	below	subset
dis-	not or do the opposite of	disagree
mis-	badly or incorrectly	misspell
uni-	one	unicycle
bi-	two	bicycle
tri-	three	tricycle

Suffix

A word part added at the end of a base word to change its meaning or part of speech.

Suffix	Meaning	Example
-ment	state or condition	contentment
-ness	state or condition	stillness
-y	being, having, able to	lucky
-ly	like or in a _____ way	safely
-er	one who does something	teacher
-or	one who does something	actor
-er	compares two things or people	quicker
-est	compares more than two things or people	quickest
-less	without	spotless
-ful	causing or full of	cheerful
-tion	the state of	celebration
-sion	the state of	decision
-able	is or can be	adorable
-ible	is or can be	reversible

Root

Part of an English word that comes from other languages such as Latin or Greek.

Prefix	Meaning	Example
bio	life	biography
graph	something written or drawn	graphics
auto	self	autobiography
port	carry	portable
dict	to say	dictate
rupt	break	erupts

Prefix	Meaning	Example
struct	build	construct
scrib/ script	write	scribble
scope	to watch or look at	microscope
tele	far off	television
phon	sound or voice	telephone
vis/vid	to see	visible

Acknowledgments

Grateful acknowledgment is made to the following sources for permission to reprint from previously published material. The publisher has made diligent efforts to trace the ownership of all copyrighted material in this volume and believes that all necessary permissions have been secured. If any errors or omissions have inadvertently been made, proper corrections will gladly be made in future editions.

From *The University of Texas at San Antonio Admission Viewbook*. Copyright © The University of Texas at San Antonio. Reprinted by permission of The University of Texas at San Antonio.

From *The Six Most Important Decisions You'll Ever Make* by Sean Covery. Copyright © 2006 by Franklin Covey, Co. Published by Simon & Schuster, Inc.

From *This Full House* by Virginia Euwer Wolff. Copyright © 2009 by Virginia Euwer Wolff. Published by HarperTeen, an imprint of HarperCollins Publishers. All rights reserved.

From *The Red Circle: My Life in the Navy SEAL Sniper Corps and How I Trained America's Deadliest Marksmen* by Brandon Webb with John David Mann. Copyright © 2012 by Brandon Webb. All rights reserved.

From "The Guys Who Got bin Laden" by Kristin Lewis from *Scholastic Scope*, September 5, 2011. Copyright © 2011 by Scholastic Inc. All rights reserved.

From *Extra Lives: Why Video Games Matter* by Tom Bissell. Copyright © 2010 by Thomas Carlisle Bissell. Published by Pantheon Books, a division of Random House, Inc.

From "Striiv: Fitness Meets Gaming, Minus the Console" by Alex Pham from *The Los Angeles Times*, October 26, 2011. Copyright © 2011 by The Los Angeles Times. Reprinted by permission of The Los Angeles Times.

From *The Hunger Games* by Suzanne Collins. Copyright © 2008 by Suzanne Collins. Published by Scholastic Inc.

Excerpts from "Why Videos Go Viral" by Bailey Johnson from the CBSNews.com website, February 28, 2012. Copyright © CBS News. Reprinted by permission of CBS News.

From "George A. Romero: 'Who Says Zombies Eat Brains?'" by Eric Spitznagel from *Vanity Fair* magazine, May 27, 2010. Copyright © 2010 by Condé Nast Publications. Reprinted by permission of Condé Nast Publications.

From "The Langoliers" from *Four Past Midnight* by Stephen King. Copyright © 1990 by Stephen King. Published by Penguin Group (USA) Inc.

From "Hollywood, Halloween, and Horror Movies—a Killer Formula" by Stuart Fischoff from *Psychology Today*, October 29, 2011. Copyright © 2011 by Sussex Publishers, LLC. Reprinted by permission of Sussex Publishers, LLC. All rights reserved.

"Frisked for Nothing" excerpted from "Why Is the N.Y.P.D. After Me?" from by Nicholas K. Peart from *The New York Times*, December 17, 2011. Reprinted by permission of The New York Times. All rights reserved.

"Police Media Report" from the City of Urbana website.

From "Small Colored World" by Terris McMahan Grimes from *Shades of Black: Crime and Mystery Stories by African-American Writers* edited by Eleanor Taylor Bland. Copyright © 2004 by Terris McMahan Grimes. Reprinted by permission of the author.

From *The Right to Freedom From Searches* by Fred Ramen. Copyright © 2001 by Fred Ramen. Published by The Rosen Publishing Group, Inc.

From "The Invisible Injury" by Sean McCollum from *Scholastic Choices*, April/May 2009. Copyright © 2009 by Scholastic Inc. All rights reserved.

From *Roughnecks* by Thomas Cochran. Copyright © 1997 by Thomas Cochran. Published by Houghton Mifflin Harcourt Publishing Company.

From "Somalia: Famine's Youngest Victims" by Cassandra Nelson from *Junior Scholastic*, December 12, 2011. Copyright © 2011 by Scholastic Inc. All rights reserved.

From *Quiet As They Come* by Angie Chau. Copyright © 2010 by Angie Chau. Published by Ig Publishing.

Credits

Cover (clockwise from tc): © Digital Vision/Getty Images, © Friedrich Saurer/Phototake, United States Naval Special Warfare (SEAL), © Thomas Barwick/Getty Images, Wook Jin Jung, © Medi-Mation Ltd/Photo Researchers, Inc., © iStockphoto/Thinkstock, © sonofpioneer/Fotolia, © Marilyn Nieves/iStockphoto; Backcover (top to bottom): © Digital Vision/Getty Images, United States Naval Special Warfare (SEAL), Wook Jin Jung, © Moodboard/Glow Images, © Randy Faris/MediaBakery, © Ted S. Warren/AP Images, Courtesy Ann C. McKee, MD, VA Boston HealthCare System, Boston University School of Medicine, © Lynsey Addario/VII; p. 2 cl: © Digital Vision/Getty Images, bl: United States Naval Special Warfare (SEAL); p. 3 t: Wook Jin Jung, cl: © Moodboard/Glow Images, cr: © Altrendo Images/MediaBakery; © Randy Faris/MediaBakery; p. 4: © Ted S. Warren/AP Images, c: Courtesy Ann C. McKee, MD, VA Boston HealthCare System, Boston University School of Medicine, b: © Lynsey Addario/VII; p. 6 tl: © Digital Vision/Getty Images, tr: United States Naval Special Warfare (SEAL), cl: © Moodboard/Glow Images, cr: © Altrendo Images/MediaBakery, bl: Wook Jin Jung; p. 7 tl: © Randy Faris/MediaBakery, tr: © Ted S. Warren/AP Images, bl: Courtesy Ann C. McKee, MD, VA Boston HealthCare System, Boston University School of Medicine, br: © Lynsey Addario/VII; p. 10 t: © Andersen Ross/MediaBakery, c: Courtesy The University of Texas at San Antonio; b: © 2012 WAMU 88.5 News, photo by Kavitha Cardoza; pp. 10–11: © Digital Vision/Getty Images; p. 12 t: © Image Source/Thinkstock, c: © Kathleen Finlay/MediaBakery, b: © iStockphoto/Thinkstock; p. 13 tl: © Medioimages/Photodisc/Thinkstock, cl: © Pemotret/Dreamstime, bl: © David De Lossy/Thinkstock, tr: © iStockphoto/Thinkstock, cr: © iStockphoto/Thinkstock, br: © Image Source/Thinkstock; p. 14 c: © Andersen Ross/MediaBakery; p. 15 b: © Jupiterimages/Thinkstock; p. 16 l: © Adam Kazmierski/iStockphoto, r: © Image Source/Thinkstock; p. 19 t: © Rubberball/Getty Images; p. 20 c: Courtesy The University of Texas at San Antonio; pp. 20–21 background: © Jason Titzer/iStockphoto; p. 22 b: © 2012 WAMU 88.5 News, photo by Kavitha Cardoza; pp. 22–23 t: © Pro777/Dreamstime; p. 26 l: © Comstock Images/Thinkstock, r: © Monkey Business/Fotolia; p. 29 c: © Alexander Raths/Fotolia; pp. 30–31 background: © Denis Jr. Tangney/iStockphoto; p. 32 t: © Tom Weber /Stocktrek Images/Corbis, c: United States Naval Special Warfare (SEAL), b: © Al Jazeera/AP Images; pp. 32–33: United States Naval Special Warfare (SEAL); p. 34 t: © Paul Chiasson, CP/AP Images, c: © Nelvin C. Cepeda/ZUMA Press/Corbis, b: © Andersen Ross/MediaBakery; pp. 36–37 t: © Tom Weber /Stocktrek Images/Corbis; p. 37 c: © Brand X Pictures/Thinkstock; p. 38 l: © Photos.com/Thinkstock, r: © Photodisc/Thinkstock, background: © fonikum/iStockphoto; p. 41 t: © Howard Lipin/The U-T San Diego/ZUMA Press; p. 42 t: United States Naval Special Warfare (SEAL), b: United States Naval Special Warfare (SEAL); p. 42–43 background: © Dean Turner/iStockphoto; p. 45 c: © Al Jazeera/AP Images; p. 46 t: © Pete Souza/ The White House/AP Images; p. 47 c: NordNordWest/Wikipedia; p. 48 t: © Comstock Images/Thinkstock, c: © Zhang Jun/Xinhua/ ZUMA Press; p. 49 r: © Michael Jarecki/Cards2Kids, l: © ZUMA Press/Newscom; p. 51 t: © Spencer Platt/Getty Images; pp. 52–53 background: © David Porter/Dreamstime; p. 54 t: Darrin Pepe, c: Wook Jin Jung, b: © Mohini Patel Glanz; pp. 54–55: Wook Jin Jung; p. 56 t: © Brand X/Thinkstock, c: © Slavenko Vukasovic/Thinkstock, b: © Gerville Hall/iStockphoto; p. 58 c: © Hocus-Focus/iStockphoto; pp. 58–59 background: Darrin Pepe; p. 60 t: © Jonathan Hill/Thinkstock, b: © Mark Herreid/Dreamstime; p. 63 t: © Chris Ratcliffe/Bloomberg via Getty Images; p. 64: Wook Jin Jung; p. 67 c: © Mohini Patel Glanz; p. 68 t: © Mohini Patel Glanz; p. 69 b: © John Woods/Canadian Press/Phototake, Inc.; p. 70 l: © James Woodson/Thinkstock, r: © Rudyanto Wijaya/Dreamstime, background: © Todor Tcvetkov/iStockphoto; p. 73 t: © Alexander Raths/Dreamstime; p. 74 b: © Ralko/Dreamstime; pp. 74–75: © Krishna Kumar/Thinkstock; p. 76 background (l): © Moodboard/Glow Images, t: © AbacaUSA/Polaris, c: Used with the permission of Nick Anderson, the Washington Post Writers Group and the Cartoonist Group. All rights reserved, b: © Lifetime Television/Courtesy Everett Collection/Glow Images; pp. 76–77 background (r): © Altrendo Images/MediaBakery; p. 78 t: © Digieye/Dreamstime, c: © Bob Daemmrich/PhotoEdit, b: © Bob Daemmrich/PhotoEdit; p. 80 tl: © Dawn Mayfarth/iStockphoto, tl: © Blue67/Dreamstime, c: © Thomas Michael Corcoran/PhotoEdit; pp. 80–81 background: © sorendls/iStockphoto; p. 81 t: © Samer Zoran Hindi/iStockphoto; p. 82 t: © Martin Harvey/MediaBakery, b: © Anne Montfort/Glow Images; p. 85 t: © AbacaUSA/Polaris; p. 86 c: Used with the permission of Nick Anderson, the Washington Post Writers Group and the Cartoonist Group. All rights reserved; pp. 86–87 background: © Iwona Rajszczak/iStockphoto; p. 89 c: © Lifetime Television/Courtesy Everett Collection/Glow Images; p. 90 b: © Bravo TV/Courtesy Everett Collection/Glow Images; p. 92 t: © Andy Gehrig/iStockphoto, c: © Ben Blankenburg/Corbis, b: © Matt Rourke/AP Images; p. 95 t: © Matt Sayles/AP Images; pp. 96–97 background: © Kiscso/Dreamstime; p. 97 b: © Antikainen/Dreamstime; p. 98 c: © Don Foley, t: © Jorge Uzon/Corbis, b: © Juice Images/age fotostock; pp. 98–99: © Randy Faris/MediaBakery; p. 100 t: © Kyle Monk/Getty Images, t: © Rob Lewine/Glow Images, t: © Claudia Rehm/Westend61/Newscom, c: © John Kobal Foundation/Getty Images, b: © Louis Quail/MediaBakery; p. 102 t: © Gordan Poropat/Dreamstime, c: © Jorge Uzon/Corbis; pp. 102–103 background: © leksustuss/Fotolia; p. 103 t: Courtesy Everett Collection; p. 104 t: © Richard G. Bingham II/Alamy; p. 107 t: © Ethan Miller/Getty Images; p. 108 b: © Don Foley; pp. 108–109 background: © Aleksandar Velasevic/iStockphoto; pp. 110–111 t: © Juice Images/age fotostock; p. 113 c: © Photosoup/Dreamstime; p. 114 t: © AJPhoto/Hôpital de Pédiatrie et de Rééducation de Bullion /Photo Researchers, Inc., r: © Hongqi Zhang/Dreamstime; p. 117 t: © West Coast Surfer/MediaBakery; pp. 118–119 background: © Sebastian Kaulitzki/Fotolia; p. 120 t: © Ashley Gilbertson/VII, c: Urbana Police Department, b (background): © Larry Mulvehill/Corbis, bl: © Wisconsin Department of Corrections/AP Images, bc: © Shari Lewis, Columbus Dispatch/AP Images, br: © Texas Department of Criminal Justice/AP Images; pp. 120–121: © Ted S. Warren/AP Images; p. 122 t: © Richard Lord/The Image Works, c: © Tony Gutierrez/AP Images, b: © Marilyn Nieves/iStockphoto; p. 125 t: © Ashley Gilbertson/VII; p. 126 tl: © Diane Macdonald/MediaBakery, cr: © Weston Colton/MediaBakery; pp. 129 t: © Ashley Gilbertson/VII; p. 130 b: © Daniel Ryan Burch/iStockphoto, c: Urbana Police Department; pp. 130–131 background: © sorendls/iStockphoto; pp. 134–135 background: © Larry Mulvehill/Corbis; p. 136 l: © Paul Hill/Thinkstock, r: © Lee Truong/Thinkstock; p. 139 t: © Alex Brandon/AP Images; pp. 140–141 background: © Sean Locke/iStockphoto; p. 142 c: CDC, b: © Medi-Mation Ltd/Photo Researchers, Inc., t: © Vernon Doucette/Boston University; pp. 142–143: Courtesy Ann C. McKee, MD, VA Boston HealthCare System, Boston University School of Medicine; p. 144 t: © sonofpioneer/Fotolia, c: © Monkey Business/Fotolia, b: © Creatas/Thinkstock; p. 146 tl: © Vernon Doucette/Boston University; pp. 146–147 t: © Mark Herreid/Dreamstime; p. 147 c: Courtesy Ann C. McKee, MD, VA Boston HealthCare System, Boston University School of Medicine; p. 148 t: © Luca Cappelli/iStockphoto; p. 151 t: © Jack Hollingsworth/Thinkstock; p. 152 c: CDC; pp. 152–153 background: © Michael Phillips/iStockphoto; p. 154 b: Courtesy Ron and Connie Stiles; p. 156 b: © Medi-Mation Ltd/Photo Researchers, Inc.; p. 158 background: © fonikum/iStockphoto, l: © drbimages/iStockphoto, r: © Shawn Roberts/Thinkstock; p. 161 t: © Ariel Skelley/MediaBakery; pp. 162–163 background: © Leslie Banks/Thinkstock; p. 164: Lynsey Addario/VII, t: © Abby Metty/World Vision, c: Joe LeMonnier © Scholastic Inc., b: © Vanessa Vick/Redux; p. 166 t: © Hanquan Chen/iStockphoto, c: © Joshua Hodge Photography/iStockphoto, b: © Jamal Aruru/AFP/Getty Images/Newscom; p. 168 b: © Abby Metty/World Vision; p. 169 b: © Laura Reinhardt/World Vision; p. 170 l: © John McAllister/Thinkstock, r: © Monkey Business/Fotolia; p. 173 t: © Laura Reinhardt/World Vision; p. 174 c: Joe LeMonnier © Scholastic Inc.; pp. 174–175 background: Central Intelligence Agency; p. 176 t: © Nastco/Thinkstock; p. 177 t: © Vanessa Vick/Redux; p. 178 b: © J. Miles Cary/Knoxville News Sentinel; p. 179 b: © Nastco/Thinkstock; p. 180 l: © Mirc3a/Dreamstime, r: © Photononstop/SuperStock; p. 183 t: © Ariel Skelley/MediaBakery; pp. 184–185 background: © Chris Schmidt/iStockphoto; p. 188 t: © PHOVOIR/Alamy, b: © Comstock/Thinkstock; p. 189 t: © Richard Schoenberg/Polaris Images, b: © Greg E. Mathieson Sr./MAI/Landov; p. 190 t: © Monkey Business Images Ltd/Thinkstock, b: © Photodisc/Thinkstock; p. 191 t: © Lions Gate/Courtesy Everett Collection, b: © Chris Pizzello/AP Images; p. 192 t: © Laurel Ent. Inc./Spelling Films Worldwide/World Vision/ABC-TV/Guy D'Alema/ The Kobal Collection, b: © Mary Evans/Ronald Grant/Everett Collection; p. 193 t: © Kay Chernush/Getty Images, b: © Rick Wilking/Reuters; p. 194 t: © CGinspiration/iStockphoto, b: © John Johnson/Fotolia; p. 195 t: © Cassandra Nelson, b: © Thomas Barwick/Getty Images; p. 196 t: © Yuriy Zelenen'kyy/Dreamstime, c: © Amy Davis/Baltimore Sun/MCT via Getty Images, b: Library of Congress; p.197 t: © humonia/iStockphoto, c: © James King-Holmes/Science Source, b: © Time Life Pictures/Getty Images; p.198 t: © Vangert/Dreamstime, c: © Ann Heisenfelt/AP Images, b: © Torsten Krueger/Thinkstock; p. 199 t: © Zoonar/Thinkstock, c: © Daniel J. Barry/Getty Images; p.200 t: © Bob Daemmrich/Alamy, c: © Patrick Aventurier/GAMMA/Getty Images; p. 201 t: © Lisa Poole/AP Images, b: © Susan Walsh/AP Images; p. 202 t: © dblight/iStockphoto, b: © Marc Lester/AP Images; p. 203 © Philippa Banks/Thinkstock, b: © Fred Bavendam/Minden Pictures/Corbis; p. 204 t: © John Amis/AP Images, b: © DL1 WENN Photos/Newscom; p. 205 t: © Alan Ashley/SCG/ ZUMA Press, b: © Nicke Hallgren/iStockphoto; p. 206 t: © Waltraud Grubitzsch/EPA via Newscom; p. 207 t: © CJ Gunther/EPA/Newscom; p. 246: © Yuriy Zelenen'kyy/Dreamstime, © Amy Davis/Baltimore Sun/MCT via Getty Images, c: Library of Congress; p. 247 c: © James King-Holmes/Science Source, © Time Life Pictures/Getty Images, c: © Vangert/Dreamstime, b: © Ann Heisenfelt/AP Images; p. 248: © Torsten Krueger/Thinkstock, c: © Zoonar/Thinkstock, c: © Daniel J. Barry/Getty Images, b: © Bob Daemmrich/Alamy; p. 249 t: © Patrick Aventurier/GAMMA/Getty Images, c: © Lisa Poole/AP Images, c: © Susan Walsh/AP Images, b: © dblight/iStockphoto; p. 250 t: © Marc Lester/AP Images, c: © Philippa Banks/Thinkstock, c: © Fred Bavendam/Minden Pictures/Corbis, b: © John Amis/AP Images; p. 251 t: © DL1 WENN Photos/Newscom, t: © Alan Ashley/SCG/ZUMA Press/Newscom, c: © Nicke Hallgren/iStockphoto, b: © Waltraud Grubitzsch/EPA via Newscom; p. 272 t: © CJ Gunther/EPA/Newscom; p. 272 t: © Digital Vision/Getty Images, b: United States Naval Special Warfare (SEAL); p. 273: Wook Jin Jung, bl: © Moodboard/Glow Images, br: © Altrendo Images/MediaBakery; p. 274 t: © Randy Faris/MediaBakery, b: © Ted S. Warren/AP Images, t: Courtesy Ann C. McKee, MD, VA Boston HealthCare System, Boston University School of Medicine, b: © Lynsey Addario/VII; p. 280 tl: © Jeffrey Vock.